Around the

World

Quiz Book

Around the World Quiz Book

Helicon

Copyright © 1998 Helicon Publishing Ltd

First published in Great Britain 1998 by

Helicon Publishing Ltd
42 Hythe Bridge Street
Oxford OX1 2EP
e-mail: admin@helicon.co.uk
Web site: http://www.helicon.co.uk

ISBN 1-85986-236-5

British Cataloguing in Publication Data
A catalogue record for this book is available
from the British Library

Printed and bound in Denmark by
Nørhaven A/S, Viborg

Contents

There are 75 geographical General Knowledge quizzes in this book. General Knowledge quizzes have even quiz numbers (2, 4, 6, etc.). The other 75 quizzes are on specialized topics, and are listed below. Numbers are quiz numbers, not page numbers.

QUESTIONS

Capital Cities

1   In 1992, Abuja replaced Lagos as capital of which African country?

2   Its name means 'New Flower' in English. What is the capital city of Ethiopia called ?

3   Which name is shared by the capital cities of Hong Kong and the Seychelles?

4   The Himalayan city of Kathmandu is the capital of which mountainous country?

5   Which holy city, the capital of Tibet, was closed to Westerners until 1904?

6   Which of the world's capital cities stands on the Potomac River?

7   Of which Indian state is Lucknow the capital?

8   The name of which European capital city translates into English as 'Log Island'?

9   Which of the world's capital cities is constructed in the shape of a bow and arrow?

10   Who designed the Indian capital of New Delhi?

Answers on page 157

General Knowledge 2

1   What term describes the frozen treeless plains of the Arctic?

2   What kind of object is a Japanese koto?

3   Which famous religious building stands on an island in the river Seine?

4   At which African city do the waters of the Blue and White Niles converge?

5   Which European country restored its monarchy in 1975?

6   What is the name of a soft white Belgian cheese with a very strong smell and flavour?

7   Which bird appears on the flag of Albania?

8   Which country has the world's highest population, currently well over one billion?

9   Which Portuguese colony was leased from Hong Kong and will be handed back in 1999?

10   What is the name of the chief island of the Seychelles?

Answers on page 157

Food Around the World 3

1　Which native East Asian plant is the richest natural vegetable food?

2　Beetroot is the main ingredient of which Russian soup?

3　What is the main ingredient in the German dish sauerkraut?

4　Which country's national dish is goulash, a tasty stew usually flavoured with paprika?

5　From which country does the spicy birds' nest soup originate?

6　What is the country of origin of Wiener schnitzel, a breaded and fried veal escalope?

7　In which European country is Gruyère cheese made?

8　In which country would you expect to be served a yoghurt-based starter called tzatziki?

9　By annual production, which is the world's most extensively grown fruit?

10　Which German city was once head of the Hanseatic League and is known for its marzipan?

Answers on page 157

General Knowledge 4

1   Which country is served by the airline QANTAS?

2   Which South African headland forms a peninsula between Table Bay and False Bay, Cape Town?

3   What in China is a sampan?

4   Which currency is shared by the countries of Algeria, Jordan, and Libya?

5   Which fast ballroom dance in 4/4 time is named after a town in South Carolina?

6   Which country is the home of the Ashanti?

7   What nationality were the members of the first successful expedition to the South Pole?

8   The Leaning Tower of Pisa in Tuscany is 55 m/180 ft high and 5 m/16.5 ft out of the perpendicular. What was the original function of the tower?

9   Where in Germany is there an annual summer festival devoted to the operas of Richard Wagner?

10   Which type of sugar has the same name as a river in Guyana?

Answers on page 157

1   Which natural monolith in the heart of Australia's Northern Territory has magical significance for the Aborigines?

2   Djaja Peak (16,503 ft/5,030 m) is the highest point in the mountainous interior of which Australasian island, the second largest in the world after Greenland?

3   Which city stands on the site of the original penal colony at Botany Bay in Australia?

4   Name the capital of the Australasian island nation of Fiji.

5   Which town in the Macdonnell Ranges of the Northern Territory is almost the exact centre of Australia?

6   What is the wine-growing area in the Lofty mountain ranges of South Australia?

7   Which Australian creature has an aboriginal name meaning 'no drink'?

8   Which sea lies between the northeastern coast of Australia and the islands of Fiji, Santa Cruz, and Guadalcanal?

9   What is the name of the arid coastal plain between Western South Australia?

10   What is the name of the large gulf lying between Northern Territorries and Queensland?

Answers on page 157

1   What is the Italian name for the city of Turin?

2   What were the two former names of the city now known as Istanbul?

3   Noah's Ark is believed to have come to rest on Mount Ararat. In which modern country is Mount Ararat to be found?

4   What is mined at Kimberley in South Africa's northern cape?

5   On which Japanese island do the cities of Tokyo and Osaka both stand?

6   Which Mediterranean island was the birthplace of Napoleon?

7   What kind of geographical feature are Cotopaxi, Etna, and Popocatépetl?

8   Which Brazilian dance became fashionable in Europe in 1989?

9   Which railway system was opened in 1904 and stretched for 3,200 miles connecting Vladivostok with Moscow?

10   Which peninsula on the south coast of Cyprus is the site of a British military base?

Answers on page 157

Foreign Names

1   The French name for this stretch of water is *La Manche*. What is the English name?

2   Known as *Hellas* in its native tongue, what is the English name of this country?

3   Which group of islands in the Aegean Sea has a name meaning 'Twelve Islands'?

4   What is the Hindi name for India?

5   What is the Russian name for Moscow, the capital of Russia?

6   Which island situated at the tip of South America has a name meaning 'Land of fire'?

7   The German name for this large European lake is *Bodensee*. What is its English name?

8   Known in Romanian as the *Dunarea* and in Hungarian as the *Duna*, what is the English name of this great river?

9   The Nepalese call it *Sagamartha* and in Tibetan it is *Mi-ti gu-ti cha-pu long-na*. What is its English name?

10   Which great river takes its name from the Indian word meaning 'Destroyer of boats'?

Answers on page 158

1   Which dry white wine is produced from grapes grown in the Loire valley of France?

2   Which is England's largest county?

3   What is the collective name for Maine, New Hampshire, Vermont, Massachussetts, Rhode Island, and Connecticut, six states settled by the Puritans from the 'old country'?

4   Which north African country uses the Dirham as its unit of currency?

5   Which islands were the subject of a war between Argentina and Britain in 1982?

6   In which European city is the headquarters of the Red Cross?

7   Which association was established in 1963 to eradicate colonialism and improve economic, cultural and political cooperation in Africa?

8   Which is the largest and deepest of the Great Lakes of North America?

9   Which British island in the South Atlantic takes its name from the day of the year on which it was discovered in 1501?

10   What is Annapurna?

Answers on page 158

Animals Around the World 9

1   Which is the main domestic animal of the people of Tibet?

2   What is the name of the marshy area of France formed by the Rhône delta, known for its white horses?

3   Famous for training pure white Lippizaner horses, in which city is this Spanish Riding School located ?

4   Queen Alexandra's birdwing, found on Papua New Guinea is the world's largest species of what?

5   Which area of Newfoundland in Canada is also the name of a breed of dog?

6   In which country can you see budgerigars living in the wild?

7   Which group of islands were named from the wild dogs discovered there by early visitors?

8   The chihuahua is a breed of small dog named after a city in which country?

9   Which group of volcanic Pacific islands are famed for their giant tortoises and have a name that means 'tortoise' in Spanish?

10   Which large ape of Borneo and Sumatra has a name meaning 'man of the woods'?

Answers on page 158

1   Of which region on the frontier between Croatia and
     Bosnia-Herzegovina is the chief town Knin?

2   Which European country boasts the world's oldest
     parliament dating from 1265?

3   On which river does the Italian city of Verona stand?

4   Which soft cheese is named after the village in
     Normandy, France where it originated?

5   Which is the most extensive glacier in Europe?

6   What was the former name of Vanuatu?

7   Which is the largest of the continents?

8   In which city is the headquarters of the United
     Nations?

9   Which Chilean port was occupied by the English naval
     adventurers Francis Drake in 1578 and John Hawkins
     17 years later?

10   Which mountain system is sometimes referred to as
     'the backbone of England'?

Answers on page 158

Islands

1   Which country is composed of 13,677 islands?

2   Which island contains the countries of Haiti and the Dominican Republic?

3   Which is the largest of the Dodecanese islands?

4   What is the name of the group of islands in the Indian Ocean between Madagascar and the east coast of Africa?

5   Which small island in the Persian Gulf is used by Iran as a deep-water oil terminal?

6   Which volcanic island appeared from the sea to the south west of Iceland in 1963?

7   Which Atlantic island was evacuated in 1961 due to volcanic eruptions?

8   On which island is the mountain known as Adam's Peak?

9   The Malvinas are a group of islands in the South Atlantic. By what name are they more commonly known in Britain?

10   Gozo and Comino are small islands making up part of which island country?

Answers on page 158

1　Mount Kosciusko is the highest point in which country?

2　Name the city founded by Arabs around AD 625 which, with a population of over 6 million, is the largest city on the African continent. The citadel containing the Muhammad Ali mosque was constructed in the 12th century by the sultan Saladin.

3　What name is given to a smooth, oval hill created by glacial drift?

4　What is the name of a people inhabiting central north Spain and the extreme southwest of France?

5　Who discovered the Victoria Falls on the Zambezi River in November of 1855?

6　In which city could you sunbathe on Bondi beach?

7　Which Indian state is responsible for the production of over 50% of India's annual tea crop?

8　What organization of Arab states was established in Cairo in 1945 to promote Arab unity, primarily in opposition to Israel?

9　The world's largest lake has a slightly misleading name. What is it?

10　Which sheikdom is the capital of the United Arab Emirates?

Answers on page 158

Places of Worship

1   Name the city where you would find the Blue Mosque.

2   Where is the spectacular Church of the Holy Family, left unfinished on his death by Antonio Gaudí?

3   In which of the world's capital cities is there a famous cathedral dedicated to St Basil?

4   The Byzantine cathedral of San Marco is in which romantic city?

5   Where in Spain is there an 11th century cathedral which was a famous medieval place of pilgrimage?

6   In which eastern country can you see the ancient golden spired Shwe Dagon Pagoda?

7   Which district of Paris, France is dominated by the basilica of the Sacré Coeur?

8   Which islet off the northwest coast of France has been the site of a Benedictine monastery since 708?

9   The Great Hassan II Mosque is the largest in the world. In which north African city is it situated?

10   In which Indian city is the Golden Temple, the sacred building of the Sikh religion?

Answers on page 159

1   Beside which river do the Indian cities of Agra and Delhi stand?

2   Gene Pitney once sang that he was *Only 24 hours from Tulsa*. In which state of the USA is Tulsa?

3   Maryland, a state of the USA was named after Henrietta Maria, wife of which English king?

4   In modern Saudi Arabia, which is the holiest city in the world of Islam, as Muhhammad, the founder of the religion was born there?

5   Which city in Canada is the world's largest French-speaking city (excluding Paris)?

6   To which country is the cassowary native?

7   Which principality has been ruled by the Grimaldi family since the 13th century?

8   Which is the smallest of the world's oceans?

9   In which town did Bernadette Soubirous see a vision of the Virgin Mary?

10   Which island in the Firth of Clyde, chief town Brodick, gives its name to a well known type of sweater?

Answers on page 159

Holiday Destinations 15

1   Which tropical Indonesian island, east of Java, is a
     popular holiday destination with over one million
     tourists annually?

2   On which island is the holiday resort of Montego Bay?

3   Which is the largest of the Canary Islands, popular
     with European holidaymakers?

4   Which ancient kingdom of southern Portugal is now a
     popular holiday resort in the modern district of Faro?

5   Name the area of Spanish coast which includes the
     holiday resort of Benidorm.

6   What is the name of the Mediterannean coast
     extending from Menton to St Tropez in France,
     renowned for its beaches?

7   What is the name of the upper valley of the river Inn in
     Switzerland, a winter sports resort?

8   Acapulco is a holiday resort in which country?

9   What is the name of the exclusive holiday island in the
     Caribbean frequented by Britain's Princess Margaret?

10   In which city is the world famous Copacabana beach?

Answers on page 159

1   What is the French name of Aachen, an ancient city in Germany?

2   What is Chicago's nickname – probably because of its open position on the shores of Lake Michigan?

3   In which country was the Buddha born?

4   Of which country do the Chatham Islands form a county?

5   Which island country is in the Indian Ocean, east of Madagascar?

6   Which Canadian river was at the centre of a gold rush in 1896?

7   In which English county are the holiday resorts of Bude, Falmouth, Newquay, and St Ives?

8   Which is the northernmost of the Greek Ionian islands, a popular holiday destination for Europeans?

9   On which river does Baghdad, capital of Iraq, stand?

10 The Channel Tunnel's high speed rail service, Eurostar, links London with Paris and which other European capital?

Answers on page 159

Lakes Around the World 17

1 The largest lake of Central America is a freshwater lake that contains fish, such as tuna and sharks, usually found only in salt water, because it was once part of the Caribbean Sea until landmasses rose around it in prehistoric times. What is its name?

2 Which lake is surrounded by the countries of Uganda, Kenya, and Tanzania?

3 Which is the largest lake to be found in Italy?

4 Which is the smallest of the five Great Lakes of North America?

5 The largest lake in central Europe is called Lake Balaton. In which country is it situated?

6 The world's highest lake lies on the border between Peru and Bolivia at an altitude of over 12,000 feet. What is its name?

7 Name the lake which lies on the northeastern boundary of Nigeria.

8 On the shores of which of the Great Lakes does the city of Chicago stand?

9 Buttermere, Windermere, and Ullswater are lakes in which region of the British Isles?

10 In which country are the group of over 120 interconnected lakes known as the Saimaa Lakes?

Answers on page 159

1   Which two countries have shores on Lake Titicaca?

2   It was the adopted home of writer Robert Louis Stevenson and its capital city is Apia. Which island nation is this?

3   Where in the world is the Kruger National Park to be found?

4   From which region of Europe did Bram Stoker's Count Dracula come?

5   What, geographically, is a caldera?

6   In which country are there four official languages, German, Italian, French, and Romansch?

7   Name the largest mountain system in North America.

8   Which Australian state has Hobart as its capital?

9   Which is the largest island in the West Indies?

10 An island off the north east coast of England is sometimes known as Holy Island. By what other name is it called?

Answers on page 159

Identify the city as quickly as possible from the clues given.

1 **a** This African capital city was founded in 1831 by Mehemet Ali.

    b It stands at the confluence of the Blue and White Niles.

    c General Gordon was killed here in 1885.

2 **a** Capital of the Tuscany region, this Italian city was founded in the 1st century BC.

    b It was ruled by the Medici family between the 15th and 18th centuries.

    c The Ponte Vecchio has spanned the Arno river here since 1345.

3 **a** This Indian city was founded in the 13th century and came into British possession in 1662 as part of the dowry of Catherine of Braganza.

    b It is the capital of Maharashtra state and has a population of over 8 million.

    c It is a major port and the centre of the Indian film industry.

4 **a** This is a major Spanish speaking industrial city of South America where you can see the famous Pink House presidential palace.

    b Founded in 1536, it stands on the south bank of the River Plate and it became the capital of its country in 1853.

    c Its name translates into English as 'Good Winds'.

5 **a** This city was founded in 1835 and named after a British prime minister.

Answers on page 160

   b Situated near the mouth of the Yarra River, it was the capital city of Australia until 1929.

   c The Olympic games of 1956 were staged here.

6 **a** Originally the site of a frontier fort, the world's first skyscraper was constructed here in 1885.

   b It is an industrial city of Illinois situated on the shores of lake Michigan.

   c It was notorious for its gangster population during the prohibition era in America.

7 **a** This is an important industrial German city on the river Rhine whose industries include textiles, plastics, and chemicals.

   b The composer Ludwig van Beethoven was born here.

   c It was the capital of West Germany between 1949 and 1990.

8 **a** The oldest city in South Africa, it was founded in 1652 on Table Bay.

   b It is the legislative capital of South Africa.

   c Table Mountain overlooks this city.

9 **a** The Jade Buddha temple of 1882 can be seen in this heavily populated Chinese city.

   b The largest city in China, it is also China's major port and deals with over 50% of China's exports and imports.

   c With a metropolitan population of over 13 million it is considered the world's most densely populated area.

10 **a** This European capital city stands on the islands of Amager and Zealand.

   b The Christiansborg Palace is used for government meetings in this city.

   c The Little Mermaid statue can be seen at the entrance to the harbour of this city.

Answers on page 160

1   After visiting which islands did Charles Darwin postulate his theory of evolution?

2   To which country do the Faroe islands belong?

3   What is the name of the Japanese art of flower arranging?

4   Which river joins the Mississippi just north of the city of St Louis?

5   Which city stands near the mouth of the Yarra River?

6   The Soviet Union, known as the USSR, broke up in 1991. Eleven of the republics established a new Union in 1992. What was its name?

7   Which Austrian city hosts an annual music festival in honour of the composer Mozart who was born there in 1756?

8   Which set of magical beliefs and practices is adhered to by 4% of the people of Haiti?

9   Which country has been ruled by Queens Beatrix, Juliana and Wilhelmina?

10   Where in the state of Virginia is the National Cemetery for the dead of the US wars?

Answers on page 160

1   Which Australian port lies at the mouth of the Swan River?

2   In which modern day country are the ports of Sidon and Tyre?

3   Name the Russian port, on the Pacific coast at the end of the Trans-Siberian railway, which is kept open by icebreakers during the winter.

4   Which port in Iran is on the Caspian Sea and is the northern terminal for the Trans-Iranian railway?

5   This city, situated on the Mediterranean, is the chief port of Egypt. What is its name?

6   Of which country is La Ceiba the chief Atlantic port?

7   The largest city in Alaska is not the capital but the chief port. What is it called?

8   Which port in western Israel was part of Tel Aviv from 1950?

9   Dar es Salaam is a city on the Indian Ocean. It is the chief sea port of which East African country?

10   This port in Natal on the Indian Ocean is the second biggest in the Republic of South Africa. What is its name?

Answers on page 160

1   Amman is the capital of a Middle-East country ruled by a king; the country is also known as the Hashemite Kingdom. Which country is this?

2   Which US state lies immediately west of Indiana?

3   Which former French territory became the Republic of Djibouti in 1977?

4   What is the capital of the Mediterranean island of Corsica?

5   In which of the former republics of the USSR is Chernobyl, scene of a serious nuclear accident in 1986?

6   Name the city where the Five Pagoda Temple can be seen.

7   Which central region of Namibia is the home of the nomadic Bantu-speaking Herero?

8   What is the former name of the Israeli seaport of Akko?

9   Which state of northeast India gives its name to a type of tea grown there?

10   Which group of islands in the far South Atlantic is a British crown colony?

Answers on page 160

1 The countries of Zanzibar and Tanganyika united in 1964 to form which present day country?

2 Which is Africa's largest country?

3 In which African country is Timbuktu?

4 Which oasis in the Western Desert of Egypt became the headquarters of the New Valley irrigation project from 1960?

5 What is the largest hydroelectric project in Africa, created as a result of the damming of the Zambezi river to form a reservoir 230 km/144 mi long in western Mozambique?

6 Which African country has a land border with only one other country, Senegal?

7 Which river flows over the Victoria Falls on the Zimbabwe–Zambia border and also forms Lake Kariba where it is blocked by the Kariba Dam?

8 Which disputed territory 100 km/60 mi wide is on the Chad–Libya frontier and was occupied by Libya in 1973?

9 Mount Toubkal is the highest peak of which range of mountains?

10 Which African country has the ports of Oran and Bohn?

Answers on page 160

1 It used to be called the European Economic Community (EEC), then it became the European Community (EC). What is its name now?

2 What was the ancient historical name of that part of the Iberian peninsula roughly equivalent to Portugal?

3 Sheba, whose queen was a character of the Old Testament, is the ancient name for which modern-day country?

4 The Colossus of Rhodes was a statue of which Greek god?

5 Name the ruined capital of Mongol ruler Genghis Khan, southwest of Ulaanbaatar in Mongolia.

6 The Philippines comprises over 7,000 islands. Which is the largest?

7 Which one of the Sunda Islands in the western Pacific is the third largest island in the world?

8 What series of Italian anti-corruption investigations, and subsequest trials, was begun in 1992?

9 The Norfolk Broads in England are man-made. How were they created?

10 Which are the two official languages of Israel?

Answers on page 160

1   Which region of the Yukon in Canada became well known after a gold rush in the late 19th century?

2   In which Canadian province is French the official language?

3   What was the name given to Nova Scotia by French settlers in 1604, from which the term Cajun derives?

4   Lake Ontario is the smallest of the five Great Lakes with Canada's largest city on its shores – which city is it?

5   Which Canadian island in the Gulf of St Lawrence became the first English colony, established in 1583?

6   Halifax is a town in Yorkshire, but it is also the name of a Canadian city – the capital of which province?

7   The St Lawrence Seaway runs from the Gulf of St Lawrence to which of the Great Lakes?

8   Which town on Lake Ontario grew from the French Fort Frontenac and was renamed in honour of George III of England?

9   Which Canadian city was, until 1886, a settlement called Granville?

10   Of which Canadian province is Edmonton the capital?

Answers on page 161

1   Of which country is Monrovia the capital?

2   Who sailed around the world in a yacht called *Gypsy Moth*?

3   Which US state is nicknamed 'Heart of Dixie'?

4   The Equator passes through many countries; which one bears its Spanish name?

5   What are Peru's two official languages?

6   Which major export of Bangladesh is used to make sacking?

7   Geographically what are harmattan, mistral, and chinook?

8   Which European country has been ruled by Harald V since 1991?

9   Followers of which religion are expected to undertake a pilgrimage known as Haji?

10   What in America is composed of the House of Representatives and the Senate?

Answers on page 161

1   Which range of mountains lies between the Sahara desert and the Mediterranean in northwest Africa?

2   Which name is shared by mountain ranges in Spain and the USA?

3   In which Scottish mountain group is Aviemore?

4   What is the name of the range of mountains separating France and Spain?

5   What series of mountain ranges lies on the southern, southeastern, and eastern borders of the Central Plateau of France?

6   Which range of mountains divides the two semi-desert areas of South Africa's Cape Province known as Karroo?

7   In which country are the Drakensberg Mountains to be found?

8   Which is the longest of the world's great mountain ranges?

9   In which country is the major mountain range called the Pindus Mountains?

10   What range of volcanic mountains in the western USA and Canada extends 1,120 km/700 mi from north California through Oregon and Washington to the Fraser River?

Answers on page 161

1   For which household commodity is the Iranian town of Isfahan well known?

2   The name of which city commemorates the arrival of Portuguese explorers on 1 January 1502?

3   Which river in western Europe rises in the Vosges mountains, France, and is canalized from Thionville to its confluence with the Rhine at Koblenz in Germany?

4   Hardanger and Sogne can be found in Norway. What are they?

5   From which country did Iceland become independent in 1944?

6   Which river with a length of 668 km/415 mi is the longest river in Italy?

7   What eastern extremity of Australia, in New South Wales, lies just south of the border with Queensland?

8   Which arid island and bird wildlife sanctuary in the Indian Ocean lies between the Monte Bello Islands and the nortwest coast of Western Australia?

9   In 1988 the Winter Olympics were held in Calgary. In which Canadian province is this?

10   To which group of islands in the Aegean Sea does Melos belong?

Answers on page 161

1   Of which Italian region is Turin the capital?

2   *The Divine Comedy* is a famous work of Italian literature. Who wrote it?

3   Which mountainous Italian region has Perugia as its capital?

4   Which town in Umbria was the birthplace of St Francis?

5   Marmolada is the highest peak in which mountain range of Northern Italy?

6   What is the name for the hot impoverished regions of southern Italy?

7   Which coastal region of northwest Italy includes the resorts of the Italian Riviera, lying between the western Alps and the Mediterranean Gulf of Genoa?

8   At what site in the Tuscan Hills, northeast Italy, were the sulphur springs used by the Romans for baths and exploited for boric acid in the 18th and 19th centuries?

9   What is the name of the Italian island at the southern entrance to the Bay of Naples?

10   What is the name of the circular lake near Naples?

Answers on page 161

1   What is the historical name for Anatolia, the Asian part of Turkey?

2   Of which autonomous region of Spain is Pamplona the capital?

3   On which continent is the Great Rift Valley situated?

4   Which country is divided into regions known as cantons?

5   The kookaburra is a species of bird native to Australia. What is its more common name?

6   Across which stretch of water did Charles Lindbergh make the first solo non-stop flight in 1927?

7   What southwestern area of the Gulf of Mexico was the site of a major oil-pollution disaster in 1979?

8   Most people would associate the Alps with central Europe, but in which country is there a mountain range known as the Southern Alps?

9   Which mineral is abundant in the springs of Tunbridge Wells, Kent, England?

10   What is the meaning of *Sendero Luminoso,* the name of the Peruvian guerilla group?

Answers on page 161

1   What colour is the circle on the Japanese flag?

2   Which botanical emblem appears on the flag of
    Canada?

3   Which is the only national flag with a map of the
    country shown on it?

4   How many stars appear on the national flag of
    Australia?

5   Which two colours appear on the flag of Greece?

6   Which is the only national flag which is not
    rectangular in shape?

7   Which country's national flag is known as 'Old
    Glory'?

8   Which country's national flag shows the Union Jack in
    the top left corner and four red stars on a dark blue
    background?

9   What colour is the cross on the national flag of
    Finland?

10 On which country's national flag is there an image of a
    cedar tree?

Answers on page 162

1   Of what is pumpernickel a German variety?

2   Which holiday islands belonging to Portugal have the same name as a type of rich sponge cake?

3   By what name was Thailand known until 1939?

4   What is the capital of the Alsace region of France?

5   With which Italian city is the Portuguese-born Franciscan monk St Anthony associated?

6   Which island country in the Indian Ocean lies off the coast of east Africa about 400 km/280 mi from Mozambique?

7   What is the name of the South African movement led by chief Buthelezi?

8   Calcutta is an Indian city built on the westernmost mouth of the delta of which river?

9   Where is Ellis Island?

10   Which Canadian city is the country's chief port on the Pacific coast?

Answers on page 162

1 Which country is the world's largest producer of tea?

2 Which Italian region is the source of the sweet wine called Marsala?

3 Which town in southwest France is the centre of a wine-growing district famous for its brandy?

4 Which fruit gives the Belgian beer Kriek its distinctive flavour?

5 What is the name of the colourless, unsweetened Greek liqueur flavoured with aniseed?

6 Which usually red, dry table wine produced in the Tuscany region of Italy is named after a range of Italian mountains?

7 Named from the Gaelic for 'small pot', what is the name given to illegally distilled Irish whiskey?

8 What type of drink is the Californian zinfandel?

9 In which American state is the Napa Valley wine-producing region?

10 Which seaport of north Yemen, near the mouth of the Red Sea, was once famed for its coffee exports?

Answers on page 162

1   Of which organization were West Germany, France, Belgium, Luxembourg, Italy, and the Netherlands the six original members?

2   What is the name of the policy of racial segregation in South Africa which ended in 1994?

3   Which Iranian port is the major refinery and shipping port for the oil industry in Iran?

4   In which country of South America are the treeless plains known as pampas?

5   Which river flows through the cities of Pisa and Florence in Italy?

6   What is the name of the crescent-shaped sweet bread rolls served in France?

7   With which American city is the confessed murderer Albert de Salvo associated?

8   Which religion recognizes the holy city of Amritsar?

9   Which Canadian city is overlooked by the Plains of Abraham?

10   What was the name of the campaign in the Gulf War, planned by the US general and supreme commander of the Allied forces, Norman Schwarzkopf?

Answers on page 162

1   In which African country is the political party UNITA active?

2   Name the system of government in which the ruler or rulers have unlimited power.

3   What is the form of government in which one person holds absolute power?

4   In which country are the Democrats and the Republicans the two main political parties?

5   Where did the Gang of Four try to seize power in 1976?

6   Which country's parliament is called the Storting?

7   What is the name for the military rulers of a country, especially after an army takeover, as in Turkey in 1980?

8   Which South African political party represents the nationalist aspirations of the country's largest ethnic group, the Zulus?

9   What is the name of the lower house of the legislature of the Republic of Ireland?

10   In which South American country is the Peronist Justicialist (PJ) party active?

Answers on page 162

1   What was the former capital of Ethiopia until 1889, when Addis Ababa became the new capital?

2   Give the German name for the Polish port of Gdańsk.

3   What is the name of a Spanish city in the Sierra Nevada, also used as the name of an independent television company in Britain?

4   What name is shared by the Texan city that was founded in 1881 as the terminus for the Texas and Pacific Railroad, and the Kansas town that was the northern terminus for the Chisholm cattle trail?

5   Of which African country is Abuja the capital?

6   Which river flows for 2,400 km/1,500 mi through Venezuela and partly defines the border with Colombia?

7   Which chain of mountains stretches the length of the Italian peninsula?

8   What colour is the cross on the national flag of Switzerland?

9   Which type of smoked sausage is named after a town in Germany?

10   Which Asian city hosted the 1988 Olympics?

Answers on page 162

1   Name one of the two landlocked countries of South
     America.

2   Which country's largest export is cocaine?

3   What is the name of the mounted cowboys of South
     America?

4   On which island is Cape Horn?

5   Which mountain stands at the entrance of the harbour
     at Rio de Janeiro?

6   What is the name of the desert of northern Chile with
     an area of around 80,000 sq km/31,000 sq mi?

7   Which channel to the south of Tierra del Fuego is
     named after the ship of Charles Darwin's famous
     voyage?

8   Which densely populated upland plateau of the Andes
     stretches from south Peru to northwest Argentina?

9   The Galapagos Islands are 500 miles from mainland
     South America. Which country do they belong to?

10   Which huge lake is partly in Bolivia and partly in
     Peru?

Answers on page 163

1   Which island group in the North Atlantic, between the Shetlands and Iceland, is a self-governing region of Denmark?

2   On which river does the city of Prague stand?

3   In which year were East and West Germany unified?

4   Which meat is the basis of the Greek dish *kleptikos*?

5   Now known as Myanmar, what was the former name of this republic?

6   Which US state, home of the Blue Ridge Mountains, was named after England's Elizabeth I?

7   What was the name of the last king of Albania?

8   In which town is the Welsh Plant Breeding Station?

9   Which evening is associated with 'trick or treat'?

10 Which city in England's West Country has a main station called Temple Meads, built by Isambard Kingdom Brunel?

Answers on page 163

1   Isfahan is a major city in which Middle-Eastern
     country?

2   Which country comprises of a group of islands in the
     Persian Gulf between Saudi Arabia and Iran?

3   What is the collective name for the eastern region of
     the Mediterranean, consisting of the coastal regions of
     Syria, Lebanon, Israel, and Turkey?

4   What was the ancient city, carved out of red rock in
     Jordan, that was forgotten by Europeans until the
     19th century?

5   Give the ancient name for the land between the Tigris
     and Euphrates rivers which is now part of Iraq.

6   What island in the Arabian Sea, part of the sultanate of
     Oman, was formerly used as an air staging post by
     British forces on their way to and from the Far East?

7   Which river flows from Lebanon through Syria and
     Turkey to the Mediterranean Sea and is used heavily
     for irrigation?

8   Which country was suspended from the Arab League
     for 10 years from 1979?

9   Which city is the capital of Lebanon?

10   Which river rises on Mount Hermon, 550 m/1,800 ft
     above sea level, and flows into the Dead Sea,
     394 m/1,293 ft below sea level?

Answers on page 163

1   Hawaii is nicknamed 'the Aloha State'. What does the Hawaiian word *Aloha* mean?

2   Which place in California is one of the worlds hottest, driest places, with temperatures reaching 51.7° C/125° F and annual rainfall of less than 5 cm/2 in?

3   What is Australia's largest state?

4   Which city was replaced as capital of Brazil by Brasília?

5   What is the name of the pleasure resort and racecourse in the Bois du Boulogne, Paris, France?

6   Which continent occupies 10% of the world's surface, contains 90% of the world's ice and 70% of its fresh water?

7   Of what electoral system are single transferable vote and party list forms?

8   The most distinctive feature of a Manx cat is its non-existent tail. From where does this breed of cat originate?

9   Who was the emperor of Japan during World War II?

10   Which French term, used in English, refers to the easing of strained relations between nations?

Answers on page 163

1   Which two Australian explorers made the first south to north crossing of the country?

2   Sir Ernest Shackleton was a famous explorer principally associated with which region of the world?

3   Eric the Red is given the credit for the discovery of which large island in the 10th century?

4   What is the name of the West Indian island where Christopher Columbus first landed in the New World in 1492?

5   The capital of the US state of Ohio has the same name as the explorer who sailed the Atlantic in 1492 – what is it?

6   Sir Richard Burton and John Speke explored which great African lake in 1858?

7   What name did William Dampier give to the island of New Guinea in 1700?

8   Which island did Captain W Mynars reach on 25 December 1643?

9   What did the aviator James Angel discover in 1935 that now bears his name?

10   Where was the British explorer James Cook killed by natives in 1779?

Answers on page 163

1   In which country does the White Nile leave Lake Victoria?

2   Of which European country was Suriname once a colony?

3   The city of Medellìn is a centre for the drugs trade. In which country is it?

4   What is the name of the Atlantic–Pacific sea route around the north of Canada?

5   Where else in the world apart from the USA and Europe is there a Disney theme park?

6   Which country consists of a group of about 700 islands and about 2,400 uninhabited cays in the Caribbean?

7   Osborne House on the Isle of Wight was built for which British monarch?

8   In which US state is Yellowstone National Park?

9   Which range of hills form a natural border between England and Scotland?

10   Which French brandy is distilled from apple cider and named after the dèpartement in northwest France where it is produced?

Answers on page 163

1   Which river flows through the cities of Belgrade, Budapest, and Vienna?

2   The city of Montevideo stands at the mouth of which well-known river?

3   In which country does the Indus rise?

4   Which river with a vast delta to the South China Sea rises as the Za Qu in Tibet?

5   Which river forms over 200 miles of the border between the countries of Colombia and Venezuela?

6   Which river drains the Great Lakes of North America?

7   The river Glomma is the principal river in which European country?

8   In which country are the rivers Clutha, Oreti, and Waitaki?

9   Which North American river flows through the Grand Canyon down to Boulder where it is blocked by the Hoover Dam to form Lake Mead?

10   Which is the longest river in Europe?

Answers on page 164

1   These indigenous inhabitants of Australia have a rich cultural tradition connected with 'Dreamtime'. Who are they?

2   Table Mountain overlooks the South African city of Cape Town. What is the name of the cloud that often hangs above it?

3   Which is the world's highest capital city?

4   What is Szechwan?

5   Which is the largest island in Greece?

6   Which country's Grand Prix is raced around the streets of Monte Carlo?

7   Which strait links San Francisco Bay with the Pacific Ocean?

8   The Arabian Sea is a branch of which tract of water?

9   In which state of the USA are the Adirondack Mountains?

10 Which city is an important trade and finance centre as well as being Florida's main Atlantic port?

Answers on page 164

1   Which is the largest of the Japanese Volcano Islands in the western Pacific Ocean with an area of 21 sq km/ 8 sq mi?

2   What is the name of the Japanese wine which is made from fermented rice?

3   What is kakiemon, a product made in Japan?

4   Translating into English as 'Divine Wind', by what name were the Japanese suicide pilots of World War II known?

5   Which Japanese city was host to the 1972 Winter Olympics?

6   What is the name of the industrial city on Honshu Island, Japan, which is also the name of a motorcycle manufactured there?

7   With what is the Japanese art of bonsai concerned?

8   What in Japan is hara-kiri?

9   What is the national sport of Japan?

10 On which Japanese island is the port of Naha?

Answers on page 164

1   What is the county town of Antrim in Northern Ireland?

2   In which state of the USA is the subtropical region of swamp known as the Everglades?

3   Who became state president of South Africa in 1994?

4   What is the English name of the *Schwarzwald*?

5   Which winter resort town of southern France hosted the Winter Olympic Games of 1992?

6   Of which Middle Eastern country is King Hussein the ruler?

7   On which Japanese city was the first atomic bomb dropped on 6 August 1945 during World War II?

8   Which English county contains an area known as the Dukeries?

9   In which American city was the world's first skyscraper built?

10   On which inland sea do the ports of Astrakhan and Baku lie?

Answers on page 164

Bays and Gulfs Around the World

1   In which bay did Captain James Cook land on his first visit to Australia?

2   The Bay of Bengal is part of which ocean?

3   What is the name of the bay between northern Spain and western France known for its rough seas?

4   Which is the largest of the inlets on the Atlantic coast of the USA, bordered by Maryland and Virginia?

5   Which bay in Cuba was the scene of a 1961 US-sponsored invasion?

6   On the north coast of which country in the southern hemisphere would you find the Bay of Plenty?

7   What deep bay on the coast of New South Wales, Australia, lies 145 km/90 mi southwest of Sydney?

8   What is the name of the inlet on the east coast of Australia, south of Sydney, which was chosen as the site for a penal colony in 1787?

9   Into which stretch of water does the Mississippi River flow?

10   What is another name for the Persian Gulf?

Answers on page 164

1   Which great river has tributaries named Nitra, Prut, Sava, and Vah?

2   In which country are both the Snowy Mountains and Blue Mountains to be found?

3   Name the part of the Mediterranean Sea that lies between Italy and Greece, to the south of the Adriatic Sea.

4   In which type of football do teams of 18 a side compete on an oval pitch?

5   Which French politician, nicknamed 'the Bulldozer', was prime minister of France from 1974 to 1976?

6   Macgillycuddy's Reeks are in Ireland. What are they?

7   Which people speak the language known as Inupiaq?

8   On which day of the year might an Italian greet you with *'Buon compleanno'*?

9   Which island group contains the islands of St Mary's, St Martin's and St Agnes?

10 Which road with a length of 2,450 km/1,522 mi, built originally by the US military in 1942, connects Fairbanks in Alaska with Dawson Creek in British Colombia?

Answers on page 164

1   In which French city does the Council of Europe sit?

2   Where in France is the city of Nice?

3   Which is the highest mountain in France?

4   For which edible product is the French town of Dijon renowned?

5   Which city of west-central France with a population of around 140,000 is famous for its fine porcelain and its ceramics industry dating back to the 18th century?

6   Where in the Dordogne River valley region of France were well preserved cave paintings from the paleolithic age discovered by schoolboy Jacques Marsal?

7   Which river in France rises in the plateau of Langres and joins the Seine at Charenton near Paris?

8   What is the French name for the Strait of Dover?

9   There are many chateaux and vineyards along the banks of the longest river in France. Which river is it?

10   Which city on the Mediterranean is the chief seaport of France?

Answers on page 165

1   What colour is the middle stripe on the Argentine flag?

2   Which river flows through Arizona's Grand Canyon?

3   Which white burgundy wine is produced near the town of the same name in the Yonne dèpartement of central France?

4   Which salty lake in the Middle East is the lowest surface point on earth at 394 m/1,293 ft below sea level?

5   Muckle Flugga, the northernmost island in the British Isles, belongs to which island group?

6   In which year did Melbourne host the Olympic Games?

7   Which town in Tennessee, USA was the scene of the Scopes monkey trial?

8   In which Middle Eastern country is the seaport of Acre?

9   Who spent the longest time as president of the USA?

10   In China it is known as the Huang He. What do we call it in English?

Answers on page 165

1   Which is the most northerly capital city on the
      European continent?

2   Between which two rivers are the Jura mountains?

3   Which Hungarian city was formed from two towns on
      opposite sides of the Danube?

4   Give the acronym used for the organization for nuclear
      research and nonmilitary nuclear energy in Europe.

5   Of which former Yugoslavian republic is Zagreb the
      capital city?

6   In which country is the mountainous region known as
      the Tyrol?

7   The European Community was created in 1957 by
      which treaty?

8   In which Polish city was the union Solidarity formed
      in 1980?

9   Which two countries are divided by the Kattegat sea
      passage?

10   Name the mountainous peninsula on the Macedonian
      coast of Greece.

Answers on page 165

1 What type of rock is granite?

2 Which is the largest of the Irish islands off County Mayo?

3 What is the name of the mountains in the Dakotas and Wyoming, USA?

4 In which city does Graceland, home of singer Elvis Presley, stand?

5 In which South American country were the first World Cup finals in football held?

6 What are the Long Man of Wilmington and the Cerne Abbas Giant?

7 Which American state has the abbreviation AK?

8 Which country was ruled by the Duvalier family from 1957 to 1986?

9 Name the Swiss artist who was a founder of the *Blaue Reiter* group in Germany from 1911 to 1912.

10 Which Greek wine is flavoured with pine resin?

Answers on page 165

1   Which country is bounded by Saudi Arabia, Oman, the Gulf of Aden, and the Red Sea?

2   Which South American country is bordered by Brazil, Colombia, and Guyana?

3   Which European country is bordered by the Czech and Slovak Republics, Germany, Hungary, Italy, and Switzerland?

4   Which African country has common frontiers with Benin, Togo, Ghana, Ivory Coast, Mali, and Niger?

5   Which is the only country to share a land border with Denmark?

6   Which Asian country shares land borders with China, Laos, and Kampuchea?

7   Which country has borders with Cameroon, Chad, Sudan, Republic of the Congo (Zaire), and Congo?

8   Which country in Central America is bordered to the north by Honduras and to the south by Costa Rica?

9   Which Middle Eastern country has borders with Syria, Iraq, Israel, and Saudi Arabia?

10   Which landlocked country in west central Europe is bounded on the east by Austria and the west by Switzerland?

Answers on page 165

1   Which town in Sarthe département, France, has an annual 24-hour motor race?

2   Which well known winter sports resort stands on the Roaring Rock River, Colorado, USA?

3   What is the name of the small town in Buckinghamshire, England, where every Shrove Tuesday local women run a pancake race?

4   The Israeli parliament, consisting of a single chamber of 120 deputies elected for a period of four years, is known by what name?

5   Which American state was bought from Russia for $7.2 million in 1867?

6   Which two continents are separated by the Ural Mountains, stretching from the Arctic Ocean to the Caspian Sea?

7   Which sea within the Mediterranean was named after the mythological father of Theseus?

8   Who became the first president of Russia after the collapse of the USSR in 1991?

9   Name the natural feature in Scotland which was the inspiration for Mendelssohn's *Hebrides* overture.

10   Which country is known to its people as Suomen Tasavalta?

Answers on page 165

What's in a Name? 55

1   The channel between Australia and Tasmania was
     named after a British explorer. Who was he?

2   Who was the Italian explorer after whom America was
     named?

3   After which revolutionary leader was the South
     American country of Bolivia named?

4   The world's highest mountain was named after which
     surveyor-general?

5   Which city of Pennsylvania is named after a British
     prime minister?

6   Which group of south Atlantic islands are named after
     a 17th-century treasurer of the British navy?

7   Which Australian capital was once called Palmerston
     but changed its name in honour of a famous naturalist?

8   After which American president was the capital city of
     Liberia named?

9   Of which Australian state, named after a queen, is
     Melbourne the capital?

10   Which Australian state capital is named after the
     consort of Britain's William IV?

Answers on page 166

1   Which Moroccan port on the Strait of Gibraltar used to be a base for Barbary Coast pirates?

2   Which country is divided into two by the Bosporus, with Istanbul its old capital in Europe, and Ankara its present capital in Asia?

3   Tallinn is a naval port and capital of which Baltic country?

4   Which mountain chain is the barrier between northern Italy and France, Germany, and Austria?

5   In which country would you find major towns called Rosario, Mendoza, and Santa Fé?

6   Which island in San Francisco Bay was the site of an almost escape-proof prison?

7   Cape Canaveral and the John F Kennedy Space Center are in America's 'Sunshine State'. Which state is that?

8   Which Saudi Arabian city is believed to contain the tomb of Muhammad?

9   Which 15th-century navigator discovered the sea route from Europe to India via the Cape of Good Hope?

10   Which association was set up in 1949 to defend western Europe and North American states against the perceived threat from the USSR?

Answers on page 166

1   Which building in Paris was erected in 1718 for Louis d'Auvergne, Count of Evreux?

2   The tomb of the wife of Shah Jahan can be visited in the Indian city of Agra. By what name is this famous building usually known?

3   In which English county is Chatsworth House, the seat of the Duke of Devonshire?

4   Which world famous building has the address 1600 Pennsylvania Avenue?

5   In which city can the twin towers of the World Trade Center be seen?

6   Which famous Parisian monument was begun by Napoleon Bonaparte and completed in 1836?

7   At 460 m/1,500 ft, Sears Tower became the tallest building in the world when it was built in 1974. In which US city is it situated?

8   In which European capital city is the Parthenon?

9   Which world famous building was purchased in 1761 by George III of England?

10   What striking shell-like building stands beneath Sydney Harbour bridge, Australia?

Answers on page 166

1   Which country mainly makes up the Horn of Africa?

2   Kampala, the capital of Uganda, is situated on the largest inland lake in Africa. What is it called?

3   What is the capital of Zimbabwe?

4   In which Canadian province has French been the official language since 1974?

5   Which would come last in an alphabetical list of the fifty states of the USA?

6   Which country comprises two enclaves on the northwest coast of the island of Borneo, bounded to the landward side by Sarawak and to the northwest by the South China Sea?

7   In which autonomous region of Spain are the cities of Cadiz and Córdoba?

8   Geographically, what are Bondi and Copacabana?

9   In the USA, moonshine, white lightning, and mountain dew are all types of what?

10   What is the name of the Japanese art of folding paper into intricate designs?

Answers on page 166

1   Which chain of islands stretches some 240 km/150 mi southwest into Florida Bay?

2   In which of the five boroughs of New York is Wall Street to be found?

3   Name the US pop artist and filmmaker who used coke bottles and soup cans as subject matter.

4   Where in the USA did an infamous 'tea party' occur in 1773?

5   What is the name of the famous geyser in Yellowstone National Park, that blows a jet of hot water into the air every 33 to 96 minutes?

6   What plantation town was established in Virginia in 1619 and eliminated by an Indian massacre three years later?

7   Of which prehistoric lake bed in Utah, is the Great Salt Lake the surviving remnant?

8   Kansas City is a twin city in that it straddles two states. There is Kansas City, Kansas and Kansas City in which other state?

9   In terms of annual average rainfall, which is the driest state of the USA?

10   In which New England state of the USA is Yale University?

Answers on page 166

1   Which is the most sacred city in the Hindu religion?

2   What is the name of the strong alcoholic drink distilled in Scandinavia from potato or grain and flavoured with caraway seeds?

3   On which island off the coast of Scotland is the town of Tobermory?

4   Which archipelago comprised of five coral atolls in the Indian Ocean is known as the British Indian Ocean Territory?

5   To what did the country of Upper Volta change its name in 1984?

6   In which country on the American continent is Mount Logan the highest point?

7   Which is the largest city in the South Island of New Zealand?

8   Hastings, Hythe, Sandwich, Romney, and Dover were collectively known in England by what term until the addition of Rye and Winchelsea?

9   Which island state of the south west Pacific lists the sale of postage stamps as one of its major exports?

10   At which Ugandan airport was there a six-day seige in 1976 after terrorists hijacked a French airliner and forced it to land there?

Answers on page 166

1   Because it is 1,609 m/5,280 ft, exactly one mile above
    sea level, which American city is nicknamed 'Mile
    High City'?

2   Which Italian city is nicknamed 'Bride of the Sea'?

3   What is the nickname for Santa Clara County in
    California, where many high-tech electronics
    companies make semi-conductors and other computer
    components?

4   Which Scottish city is nicknamed 'Granite City'?

5   Which Asian capital city is known as 'the Forbidden
    City'?

6   Which European capital city is nicknamed 'City of
    Light'?

7   Which Scottish city is nicknamed 'Auld Reekie' from
    the thick low-lying clouds that used to hang over it?

8   Which Belgian city is known as the 'Venice of the
    North'?

9   Which fishing village and resort on the Algarve coast
    of southern Portugal is known as 'St Tropez of the
    Algarve'?

10 Which sea within the Arctic Ocean is known as the
    'great ice cellar'?

Answers on page 167

1   According to Robert Browning, which German town did the Pied Piper rid of a plague of rats?

2   Which people are credited with the invention of the game of lacrosse?

3   Which is the only country of South America whose official language is not Spanish?

4   An anorak is a warm heavy jacket with a hood. Which language does the word *anorak* come from?

5   To which country does the airline Lufthansa belong?

6   To the followers of which religion is the Ganges a sacred river?

7   Which island on the Bay of Naples is famous for its Blue Grotto?

8   Which small breed of dog is named after a city and state of Mexico?

9   Of which country is Chittagong the major port?

10 Of which Irish county is Ennis the county town?

Answers on page 167

Seas and Oceans Around the World 63

1   In which part of the world are the Ross and Weddell seas?

2   By what name is the Solomon Sea better known?

3   Which sea lies between China and Korea?

4   Which sea connects with the Mediterranean via the Bosporus and the Dardanelles?

5   Which sea would you cross on a flight from Stockholm to Riga?

6   On which sea can you reach the world's lowest point below sea level?

7   Which is the world's second largest ocean?

8   Which inland sea between Kazakhstan and Uzbekistan is fast disappearing because the rivers that feed it have been diverted and dammed?

9   Which sea, part of the north Atlantic, is noted for the vast amount of seaweed floating on its surface?

10 The Kara Sea, the Laptev Sea, and the Beaufort Sea all lie within which greater body of water?

Answers on page 167

1   Which city, 900 m/3,000 ft above sea level, is the centre of Brazil's coffee industry?

2   On which island does the city of Copenhagen stand?

3   Which Italian city, famous for its art and architecture, is the capital of Tuscany?

4   After which French king was the state of Louisiana named?

5   Which sea off the Canadian coast was named after a British admiral who also gave his name to a well known scale?

6   Which city in Michigan is the headquarters of Ford, Chrysler, and General Motors, hence its nickname 'Motor City'?

7   What is the Muslim equivalent of the Red Cross aid agency?

8   Which sultanate is bordered on all sides by the Sarawak territory of Malaysia?

9   What is the usual name for the Sea of Cortés?

10   Which area of France is known for the breeding of white horses and black bulls?

Answers on page 167

1 Which country in east central Asia is bounded north by Russia and south by China?

2 In which country are Bat-Yam and Holon?

3 What is the English name for Sulawesi, an island of Indonesia?

4 Which city and seaport is the capital of Sri Lanka?

5 Of which country is Vientiane the capital?

6 Which Asian island is the second largest in the world?

7 How many individual emirates comprise the United Arab Emirates?

8 Which Asian country is sometimes referred to as the 'Roof of the World'?

9 On which island is the region of Sarawak?

10 Papua New Guinea occupies the eastern part of the island of New Guinea. Which country occupies the western part?

Answers on page 167

1   Which mining town in New South Wales, Australia, is known as 'Silver City' because of the rich silver deposits found there?

2   Which historic Belgian town is the capital of West Flanders province?

3   Bujumbura, the capital city of Burundi, is situated at the northern end of which large African lake?

4   Which is Zimbabwe's second city?

5   What is the present name of the city which has previously been known as Byzantium and Constantinople?

6   What is the capital of the Mediterranean island of Sardinia?

7   Which Middle Eastern country's only port is called Aqaba?

8   Name the US architect who introduced his famous 'prairie house' style in the 1890's, and later designed New York's Guggenheim Museum.

9   Which is the third largest of the Channel Islands after Jersey and Guernsey?

10   In which county are England's largest lake and highest mountain situated?

Answers on page 167

1   Which is the world's second highest mountain after Everest?

2   Which South African city is overlooked by Table Mountain?

3   Named after an assassinated president, which is the highest mountain in the Bitterroot Range of the Rocky Mountains, USA?

4   Which is the highest mountain in Scotland's Grampian range?

5   Which Greek mountain was considered to be the home of the gods in ancient times?

6   Of which North African mountain system is Mount Toubkal the highest point?

7   Which is the highest peak of the Caucasus range?

8   Which European mountain is known for its North Face which is notoriously difficult to climb?

9   The highest mountain in the USA stands in the state of Alaska. What is its name?

10   Which mountain also known as Mont Cervin was first climbed in 1865 by Edward Whymper?

Answers on page 168

1   Which socialist ideology is based on the philosophy that government should be by the people, for the people, usually attained by a revolution?

2   Which country's capital city is situated on a tributary of the Murrumbidgee River?

3   In which country does the Amazon river rise?

4   In which Italian city could you have originally heard a barcarole being sung?

5   Which chocolate cake filled with cherries is named after a wooded area of Germany?

6   What is the name of the notorious penal colony that lies off French Guiana?

7   Which famous building associated with the performing arts was designed by Jorn Utzon?

8   What is the nickname of the largest city of the USA?

9   Which is the largest of the ten provinces of Canada?

10   Until 1972, the Boyoma Falls on the upper Zaïre River were named after a British explorer. What were they called?

Answers on page 168

1   Its former name was Calpe. Where is it?

2   Which west African country used to be called the Gold
        Coast because of the alluvial gold washed down in the
        river?

3   Until 1966 it was called Leopoldville; what is its new
        name?

4   What was the former name of the Vietnamese city now
        known as Ho Chi Minh City?

5   What was the former name of Iran?

6   Which African country was formerly known as
        Abyssinia?

7   Which country in the Indian Ocean had the former
        name Ceylon?

8   By what name was the New York borough of Staten
        Island known until 1991?

9   What was the former name of Tasmania?

10   Which European capital city was once known as
        Christiania?

Answers on page 168

1   Give an alternative name for Lake Malawi.

2   The Zambezi and which other river defines the border of Matabeleland?

3   In which American state is the city of Chicago to be found?

4   Through which range of mountains did writer Robert Louis Stevenson travel with a donkey?

5   What is the English name of the city of Helsingfors?

6   What is the name for the two waterfalls on the Canada–USA border which lie between lakes Erie and Ontario?

7   What geographically is Okeechobee?

8   Which mountain in Thessaly did the ancient Greeks believe to be the home of the gods?

9   What is the name of the triangular Russian musical instrument with three strings?

10   It is known by the Maoris as Aorangi. What is the English name of this New Zealand mountain?

Answers on page 168

1	What shingle bank extends 19 km/11 mi along the coast of Dorset, England, from Abbotsbury to the Isle of Portland?

2	Which is the largest lake in the British Isles?

3	Which island and ferry port is connected to Anglesey by road and rail bridges?

4	Where in Britain is Burger Hill, site of the world's most productive wind-powered generator?

5	What is the name of the highest point in England's Peak District?

6	Douglas is the capital of which island off the British coast?

7	Which island, the largest of the Inner Hebrides, was joined to the Scottish mainland by a new toll bridge in 1995?

8	In which county is Piltdown, site of a famous archaeological hoax?

9	In which county of Northern Ireland are the towns of Portadown and Lurgan?

10	What is the collective name given to the islands of Inisheer, Inishmaan, and Inishmore?

Answers on page 168

1   What nickname is given to the city of Nashville because of its connection with the recording industry?

2   Which international organization, with offices in 43 countries, fights for human rights throughout the world?

3   Which lake situated between Lake Maggiore and Lake Como lies partly in Italy and partly in Switzerland?

4   The world's fastest ball game is the game of pelota. Played with a wickerwork basket, which country does it originate from?

5   Which port of northern Russia, its chief timber-exporting port, is blocked by ice for six months of each year?

6   The US gold bullion depository is situated in the state of Kentucky. What is it called?

7   Which Irish town gives its name to a five-line humorous verse?

8   What is the name of the mountainous western section of North America which runs parallel to the Rocky Mountains and the coastal ranges?

9   What is the English name for the Danish port of Helsingør, the setting for Shakespeare's Hamlet?

10 Which peninsula in the Philippines was defended against the Japanese in World War II by US and Filipino troops under General MacArthur between 1 January and 9 April 1942?

Answers on page 168

The Mediterranean   73

1   To which island group do Majorca and Minorca
     belong?

2   Which Mediterranean island is divided in two by the
     Attila Line?

3   Which Greek island is the largest of the Cyclades?

4   Which island holds the main base of the French
     Foreign Legion?

5   Which is the largest island in the Mediterranean Sea?

6   In which sea within the Mediterranean are the
     Sporades and Cyclades islands situated?

7   In which Cypriot resort will you find the 'Tomb of the
     Kings'?

8   Sardinia is the second largest island in the
     Mediterranean. It is a special autonomous region of
     which country?

9   Of which island is Valetta the capital?

10   What is the better-known name of the group of seven
     volcanic islands off the Sicilian coast sometimes
     called the Aeolian Islands?

Answers on page 169

1 Which country is represented at Rugby Union by a team known as 'the Pumas'?

2 On which inland sea do Russia and Turkey have shores?

3 Which European country is also known as the Hellenic Republic?

4 In which city on the Mississippi River, USA, is the Gateway Arch?

5 What is the nationality of a person born in Lombardy?

6 In which US state are the towns of Fairbanks and Anchorage?

7 Who was the first person to fly across the English Channel, a feat he accomplished on 25 July 1909?

8 At which island airport did the world's worst aircraft disaster occur in 1977?

9 Which South American country is the world's largest producer of copper?

10 Which type of food is named after a northern German city on the river Elbe?

Answers on page 169

Where Is It?   75

1   Chernobyl was the site of a nuclear accident in 1986; in which country is it?

2   *Casablanca* is the title of a well-known film starring Humphrey Bogart. In which country is the town of this name?

3   Waterloo was the scene of a famous battle fought in 1815. In which country is it?

4   Guadalcanal was the site of fierce fighting during World War II. In which group of islands is it?

5   Herb Alpert was backed on several of his songs by the Tijuana Brass. Where is Tijuana?

6   In which country is Transylvania, home of the vampire legends?

7   'The Girl From Ipanema' was a popular tune of the 1960s. In which country is Ipanema?

8   Timbuktu is always cited as a very distant and outlandish place. Where is it?

9   Fez is an African city which gives is name to a type of tassled hat. In which country is it?

10   The Crimea is famous as the scene of a war in the middle of the last century which included the famous Charge of the Light Brigade. Which country does it belong to?

Answers on page 169

1   Which country is the world's major rice producer?

2   Which river in the USA is the main arm of the great river system which drains the USA between the Appalachian and the Rocky Mountains?

3   In which Swiss mountain resort could you see people descending the famous Cresta run?

4   In which European country do the Magyars make up 92% of the population?

5   What is the nationality of I M Pei, the architect who designed Asia's tallest building?

6   Which English town did the Romans call Verulamium?

7   Which district in America, situated on the Potomac River and coextensive with the city of Washington, is the seat of the federal government?

8   Which two Middle Eastern countries fought a war from 1980 to 1988?

9   In 1965 he declared his country independent under white rule, and he served as prime minister of Rhodesia between 1964 and 1979. Who is he?

10   What type of alcoholic drink is the Spanish Amontillado?

Answers on page 169

1   Which volcano was responsible for the destruction of Pompeii?

2   In what country is the volcano Aconcagua, the highest peak in the New World?

3   The eruption of which Indonesian volcano caused 36,000 deaths in 1883?

4   Which Mexican volcano began a seven-year series of eruptions in 1943?

5   Which volcano in the Lipari islands erupted violently in 1930 and 1966?

6   Which Sicilian volcano is the highest in Europe?

7   What is the name of the active volcano situated to the south of Quito in Ecuador?

8   Which volcano erupted in Washington state, USA, in 1980?

9   On which island is Mauna Loa, the world's largest active volcano crater?

10 The world's southernmost active volcano stands on Ross Island in the Antarctic. What is its name?

Answers on page 169

1   Which US state is known as the 'Land of Enchantment'?

2   Which river in southeast Australia is a tributary of the river Murray, joining it at Wentworth?

3   On which of the Greek islands did Bacchus find Ariadne according to legend?

4   In which part of northwest France is the Breton language spoken?

5   What is the dominant classical language of the Indian subcontinent?

6   Which is the only French-speaking republic in the Americas?

7   Where does bossa nova dance music originate?

8   In which city is the world famous La Scala opera house?

9   What name is given to the annual festival of music and poetry held in Wales?

10   On which Irish racecourse in County Kildare are the five Irish classics run?

Answers on page 169

1   In which country was Milton Obote overthrown by Idi Amin in 1971?

2   Which country revolted against its communist government and Soviet alliance in October 1956, resulting in occupation by Soviet tanks?

3   Which British king was dethroned by the Glorious Revolution?

4   In which African country was there a military coup on 6 April 1985 while President Nimeiri was out of the country?

5   Where in Beijing, China, did pro-democracy students stage an unsuccessful protest in 1989?

6   The Pitcairns, in the South Pacific, are the islands where nine mutineers settled in 1790. On which ship did they mutiny?

7   Salvador Allende was killed during a coup by the army in 1973 in which South American country?

8   In which country was Nicolae Ceausescu executed after an army uprising in 1990?

9   In which country was South American revolutionary Che Guevara born?

10   In which country were a group of revolutionaries known as the Nihilists active in the years 1855–81?

Answers on page 170

1   Which is the busiest airport in France?

2   The Amazon rainforest is the wettest region on earth.
    To the nearest half metre or foot, what is the average
    rainfall per year?

3   What is the approximate population of the Falkland
    Islands?

4   Which modern country did the Romans call Lusitania?

5   Which island of the Chagos Archipelago in the Indian
    Ocean is named after its Potuguese discoverer?

6   Which former Dutch colony became independent in
    1945 as Indonesia?

7   Which river in Nigeria is the largest tributary of the
    river Niger, with a length of 1,400 km/870 mi?

8   On which American Island was there a major nuclear
    accident in 1979?

9   What is the written statute containing all the
    fundamental laws of the USA?

10 In which coastal town can you visit the Library of
    Wales?

Answers on page 170

1   Which islands in the southwest Pacific lie between
    Micronesia to the north, and Polynesia to the east?

2   Which is the smaller of the two main islands of New
    Zealand?

3   What is another name for Banaba, an island belonging
    to Kiribati?

4   What is the former name of Tuvalu, a group of islands
    in the western Pacific Ocean?

5   What coral island in the mid-Pacific lies between the
    Marshall Islands and Hawaii?

6   Which area of the Pacific Ocean, between northern
    Australia and Indonesia, is bounded by the Timor Sea
    in the west and the Coral Sea in the east?

7   To which island group does Tahiti belong?

8   Tonga, a country of 169 islands in the south Pacific,
    has another popular name. What is it?

9   The Great Barrier Reef is a marine national park off
    the coast of which Australian state?

10 Which arm of the North Pacific Ocean lies between
    the Kamchatka Peninsula and Sakhalin, and is
    bordered to the south by the Kuril Islands?

Answers on page 170

1   Which famous Moroccan port has the Arabic name Dar el-Beida?

2   Which is the smallest of the states of the USA?

3   Name the country founded by Muhammad Ali Jinnah.

4   What name is given to the flat treeless Argentine plains between the Andes and the Atlantic?

5   What political award, established in 1949, is given annually to those serving European cooperation?

6   Alan Paton wrote a book entitled *Cry the Beloved Country*. Which was the country referred to in the title?

7   In which country did the art of flower arranging known as ikebana originate?

8   Philadelphia and Pittsburgh are the two largest cities, Harrisburg is the capital, and Hershey's Chocolate World is a big attraction – in which US state are they?

9   Prince Edward Island is a province in which Commonwealth country?

10   Which city is the capital of the state of Queensland, Australia?

Answers on page 170

1   Which colourful desert in Arizona is part of the
     Petrified Forest?

2   The Atacama desert lies in which South American
     country?

3   Which African desert is inhabited by the nomadic San
     people?

4   Which desert of Sudan extends from the river Nile
     eastwards to the Red Sea?

5   What is the name of the large desert found in
     Turkmenistan?

6   Which vast desert lies in Mongolia and Northern
     China?

7   What is Africa's – and the world's – largest desert?

8   What is the desert in southern Israel that tapers to the
     port of Eilat?

9   Edwards Air Force Base, famous as the landing place
     for the American space shuttle, is situated in which
     Californian desert?

10   In which of the world's deserts does the small fox
     known as the fennec live?

Answers on page 170

1 One of Rudyard Kipling's *Barrack-Room Ballads* is entitled *Mandalay*, in which an ex-soldier dreams of the road to Mandalay. Of which country was Mandalay once the capital?

2 Which tiny island in the mid-Atlantic is a British colony? Its capital is Hamilton.

3 Captain Cook called them the Sandwich Islands. What is their name now?

4 On which island can you see huge carved stone heads or *maoi*?

5 What term is sometimes used to describe the developing countries of Africa, Asia, and Latin America?

6 On which of the Canary Islands did the artist César Manrique create his volcanic cave architecture?

7 What is the name of the indirect system by which the president and vice president of the USA are elected?

8 Which city is the capital of the Italian region of Lombardy?

9 After which former president was the highest peak in the USA named?

10 Where in Hampshire, England has there been a military barracks since 1854?

Answers on page 170

1   In which country was a war fought between the years 1950–53?

2   From which French port were 337,131 allied troops evacuated in May and June 1940?

3   Which German city was the location of Nazi rallies and later the location of the trials of Nazi war criminals?

4   Into which European country were Bohemia and Moravia incorporated after World War I?

5   Which country did Germany annexe in the so-called Anschluss of 1938?

6   In which country was a civil war fought between 1936 and 1939?

7   Which two Central American countries fought the 'soccer war' in 1969?

8   What was ceded to Britain in 1713 as part of the settlement of the War of the Spanish Succession?

9   Which country was invaded in 1990 precipitating the Gulf War?

10   Which Dutch city was the scene of an airborne invasion of allied forces in September of 1944, the incident being the subject matter of the film *The Longest Day*?

Answers on page 171

1   Name the site of a nuclear power station on the Alabama River, central Alabama, USA.

2   What is the official language of Brazil?

3   Name the structure that was knocked down in 1989 after 28 years of dividing a city.

4   Which river flows through Washington DC?

5   What was the name of the empire ruled by the Turks from 1453 to 1922?

6   The USA has a government that has powers over national issues while the individual states have local autonomy. What is the name for this type of government?

7   In which country is the Toltec city of Chichen Itzá?

8   Which river, second longest in the world, drains almost half the land mass of South America?

9   Which small sovereign state forms an enclave in southern France with the Mediterranean Sea to the south?

10   Which creature, discussed since the 15th century, boosts Scottish tourism by £5 million a year?

Answers on page 171

1 Which city in India gave its name to a style of riding breeches?

2 By population, which is the largest city of India?

3 Which Indian city has become the centre of a thriving film industry known as Bollywood?

4 What was the former name of the state of Tamil Nadu?

5 What is the name of the east coast of Tamil Nadu which lies between the Kistma River delta in the north and Point Calimere in the south?

6 In which cave temples dating back to the 4th century can you see several sculptures including one of Siva and Parvati playing chess?

7 What former part of Jammu state in the north of British India has a largely Muslim population, and was ruled by a Hindu maharajah who joined it to the republic of India in 1947?

8 What is the name of the region that lies west of the Anamalai Hills in southern India which was formerly a princely state?

9 What is Nanga Parbat?

10 In which Indian city do Hindus hold the festival of the Jar of Nectar of Immortality (Khumbh Mela) every 12 years?

Answers on page 171

1   In which French town did the young peasant girl
       Bernadette Soubirous see a vision of the Virgin Mary?

2   Which sport takes place at Watkins Glen in the USA?

3   The official world championships of which unusual
       sport are held annually in Calveras, California?

4   What term describes a country governed by the
       people, usually through elected representatives?

5   The failure of which crop caused famine in Ireland in
       1845?

6   In which year did Captain James Cook first visit
       Australia?

7   Which environmental pressure group was founded in
       the UK in 1971?

8   Which river, flowing from the Rocky Mountains to the
       Gulf of Mexico, forms 2,400 km/1,500 mi of the
       USA–Mexican border?

9   Which bird was seen alive for the last time on the
       island of Mauritius in 1681?

10   What name is given to the study of earthquakes?

Answers on page 171

1   Which Scottish waterway links the North Sea with the Atlantic Ocean?

2   Which canal links the Red Sea to the Mediterranean Sea?

3   What is the name of the canal connecting the great lakes of Ontario and Erie?

4   What is the name of the system of rivers and canals in Sweden stretching from the Kattegat to the Baltic Sea?

5   The world's longest canal runs for 1,600 km/1,000 mi through China from Beijing to the Chang Jiang (Yangtze-Kiang) river valley. What is its name?

6   Which 203 km/126 mi long canal connects Lake Ontario and the Ottawa River in Canada?

7   What is the name of the ship canal connecting the cities of Liège and Antwerp?

8   Which country gives its name to a canal which links the Caribbean Sea with the Pacific Ocean?

9   What is the name of the principal waterway of Venice?

10   Which canal was built by Germany in the years before World War I to link the Baltic with the North Sea?

Answers on page 171

1 Daniel Defoe based his most famous book *Robinson Crusoe* on the real-life experiences of Alexander Selkirk, who was shipwrecked on which island?

2 The geographical centre of North America is in a town called Rugby. In which US state is it?

3 Which city whose name means 'sheltered bay' in Hawaiian, is the capital of Hawaii?

4 Much used during the 1980s, what is the Russian word meaning 'openness'?

5 What kind of mammal is a bandicoot?

6 In the UK the House of Commons and House of Lords are collectively referred to as the Houses of Parliament. What is the name given to the US Senate and House of Representatives?

7 What is the capital city of Ecuador?

8 Which infamous small island is in San Francisco Bay, USA?

9 Which gas in the atmosphere is responsible for increased global warming?

10 Which Scottish fishing town in Tayside is renowned for its 'smokies'?

Answers on page 171

1   In which European country is Gouda cheese made?

2   Give the term that describes land reclaimed from the sea in the Netherlands.

3   What is the official name of Luxembourg?

4   Give another name for 'the Low Countries' (Belgium, the Netherlands, and Luxembourg).

5   What is the official language of Luxembourg?

6   For which commodity is the Dutch town of Delft well known?

7   In which of the Low Countries is the region of Flanders?

8   Which is Belgium's 'City of Flowers'?

9   What is the French name for Brussels, capital of Belgium?

10   Which Dutch port is the biggest oil-refining centre in the world?

Answers on page 172

1   In which American city do the famous Red Sox
     baseball team play?

2   Which Italian city is overlooked by Mount Vesuvius
     with the ruins of Pompeii at its foot?

3   In which modern-day country is the area covering the
     ancient city of Babylon?

4   In which country is the well known spa town of
     Baden-Baden?

5   Which island of the Cyclades, the smallest of the
     group, is said to be the birthplace of the god Apollo?

6   Give the present-day name of the island in the Indian
     Ocean which was known as 'Serendip' by Arab spice
     traders.

7   Which island 32 km/20 mi long lies off the coast of
     Cape Cod, Massachussetts, USA?

8   Which town on the Suffolk coast in England is the site
     of an annual music festival founded by Benjamin
     Brittan?

9   In which continent are the Altai Mountains?

10   What is the name of the hill of over 244 m/800 ft
     overlooking the Scottish city of Edinburgh?

Answers on page 172

1   Which was the Canaanite town whose walls fell at the blast of Joshua's trumpets?

2   Which Syrian city mentioned in the Bible is said to be the oldest continually inhabited city in the world?

3   Which ancient region of Palestine is referred to in the Bible as the 'Promised Land'?

4   *The Last Judgement* was painted by Michelangelo in the years 1536–41. Where can it be seen?

5   Which town in the West Bank is the traditional birthplace of Jesus?

6   Which kingdom ruled in biblical times by King Herod is now part of southern Israel and southwest Jordan?

7   On which mountain did Moses receive the Ten Commandments from God?

8   In which Turkish town was St Paul said to have been born?

9   Where according to the Bible will the last great battle between good and evil take place?

10   What is the alternative name of Lake Tiberias?

Answers on page 172

1　What is the name of the Alaskan channel in which the *Exxon Valdez* caused one of the biggest shipping oil spillage disasters in 1989?

2　Which countries provide the five permanent members of the United Nations Security Council?

3　Which great river of Africa is also known as the Crocodile River in its upper reaches?

4　Cuba is the largest of the islands of the West Indies. Which island group is it a part of?

5　For which product is the Iranian town of Ardabil renowned?

6　Which two countries were created on 1 January 1993 upon the dissolution of the state of Czechoslovakia?

7　In which country is the industrial city of Bangalore?

8　In which mountain range is Ben Nevis situated?

9　Which Canadian bay of the Atlantic coast between New Brunswick and Nova Scotia has the world's greatest tidal range with a variation of around 18 m/60 ft between high and low tides?

10　On which island are the New York boroughs of Queen's and Brooklyn?

Answers on page 172

1   In which country can you travel on public rail transport known as TGV?

2   Which well-known railway system connects the east and west coasts of Canada?

3   Which German car designer developed the VW Beetle and is now better known for prestige sports cars?

4   What is the country of origin of a car bearing the international letters DK?

5   In which European country are Saab cars manufactured?

6   It's an opulent type of car, but was originally a rough cloak worn by shepherds in a former French province. What is it?

7   What is the name of the national bus company, founded in Hibbing, Minnesota, that runs services across the USA?

8   What distinguished the Japanese tanker *Shin-Aitoku-Maru*, launched in 1980?

9   In which city could you travel on public transport known as *vaporetti*?

10   Which country has the world's largest merchant navy?

Answers on page 172

1   Which French city, capital of the Limousin region, is the centre of the modern porcelain industry?

2   In which country is the Serengeti Game Reserve?

3   What is the capital city of Afghanistan?

4   Where in the world are the Plains of Abraham?

5   Which is the oldest city of Germany, having been founded in 38 BC by the Romans?

6   Europe's largest oil port, Sullom Voe, is found in which group of islands off the Scottish coast?

7   Name the southeast Asian city where you can see the temple of the Emerald Buddha.

8   Which of the world's capital cities stands on the river Tigris?

9   Which river has its source in the Black Forest of Germany and its outflow in a delta on the Black Sea?

10   From which country does Varig airlines operate?

Answers on page 172

1   What happened in San Francisco in 1906?

2   Which Moroccan city was devastated by an
      earthquake on 29 February 1960?

3   In which Islamic republic were over 30 million people
      made homeless by monsoon rains in 1988–89?

4   In 1900 a hurricane caused the deaths of between
      6,000 and 8,000 people in Galveston, USA. In which
      state is Galveston?

5   Which Icelandic volcano has been causing widespread
      destruction since the first of 14 eruptions occurred in
      the year 1104?

6   In which country were 1,524 people killed by a cloud
      of poisonous gas after an underwater explosion?

7   Which type of natural disaster killed 5,000 people in
      the Peruvian town of Huaras in December 1941?

8   The 'Black Death' was an epidemic which swept
      through Europe in the mid-14th century. What was the
      disease that caused it?

9   Which American state contains the San Andreas Fault,
      which causes devastating earthquakes?

10   Where in India did a lethal gas leak kill over 2,000
      people in 1984?

Answers on page 173

1   Which small atoll in the Marshall Islands has given its name to a diminutive type of swimwear?

2   Of which Indian state is Patna the capital?

3   Of which Australian city is Fremantle the port?

4   What is the name of the hot wind that blows south from the Sahara desert across southern Italy?

5   Which is the largest island of Bermuda?

6   This country's name means 'city of the lion' in Sanskrit. Which country is it?

7   The meat packing port of Fray Bentos is particularly associated with corned beef. In which South American country is it situated?

8   Italy's largest lake is also a popular tourist resort. What is it called?

9   Which is the largest of the six New England states of the USA?

10   On which large Mediterranean island are the Troodos mountains?

Answers on page 173

1   What is the name of the channel between Sumatra and
       the Malay Peninsula?

2   Which strait lies between Chile and the island of
       Tierra del Fuego?

3   What is the name of the strait separating the Island of
       Taiwan from mainland China?

4   Which strait lies between Greenland and Baffin
       Island?

5   Which strait separates the island of Anglesey from the
       mainland?

6   Which narrow stretch of water separates Spain and
       North Africa?

7   The Strait of Messina separates which island from the
       mainland of Italy?

8   The strait separating Asia and America is named after
       its Danish discoverer. What is it called?

9   What is the name of the strait dividing North Island
       and South Island, New Zealand?

10   What is the name of the strait joining the Black Sea
       with the Sea of Marmara, and forming part of the
       water division between Europe and Asia?

Answers on page 173

1 What name is given to the area of eastern England including Norfolk and Suffolk along with parts of Cambridgeshire and Essex?

2 Which of the world's lakes contains the most freshwater?

3 For which industry is the Australian town of Ballarat particularly known?

4 What is Benbecula?

5 Which nation captured the Indian state of Goa in 1510?

6 The islands Gozo and Comino are a part of which state?

7 Maclear's Beacon at 1,087 m/3,568 ft is the highest point on which well-known mountain?

8 With the production of which type of weapon is the Spanish town of Toledo primarily associated?

9 Port Said stands at the northern end of which waterway?

10 Syracuse is the name of a city in New York State, USA, and also the name of an ancient port of which Mediterranean island?

Answers on page 173

1   Name China's longest river.

2   Which new policy in 1958 was an attempt to achieve 'true communism' in China?

3   What is the name of the currency of China?

4   Which fortification, 2,250 km/1,450 mi long and dating from the third century BC, is now one of the world's major tourist attractions?

5   Name the range of mountains separating the Tarim Basin from the Tibetan plateau of southwest China.

6   This region of northeast China comprises the provinces of Jilin, Liaoning, and Heilongjiang. What is it called?

7   Which city on the Yangtze-Kiang River was capital of China between 1937 and 1946?

8   Which port, handling about 50% of the country's imports and exports, is the largest city in China?

9   This port in southeast China is known by its Mandarin name of Xiamen. What was its former name?

10 Name the peninsula on the Chinese coast that formed part of the former British colony of Hong Kong.

Answers on page 173

1 In which Dublin college can the illuminated book of the Gospels, the *Book of Kells*, be seen?

2 The largest inland port of Europe, this German industrial city stands at the confluence of the rivers Ruhr and Rhine. What is its name?

3 In which Russian city were Tsar Nicholas II and his family murdered by revolutionaries in 1918?

4 Which collective name is given to the countries of Estonia, Latvia, and Lithuania?

5 Into which stretch of water do the Ganges and Irrawaddy rivers flow?

6 By what name is the former Portuguese West Africa now known?

7 Which is the smallest of the provinces of Canada?

8 Which stretch of water separates mainland Scotland from the Western Isles?

9 Which port on the Mississippi is regarded as the traditional birthplace of jazz?

10 Of which island nation is Andros the largest island?

Answers on page 173

1   Which Caribbean island, together with the
     neighbouring island of Trinidad, forms a country in
     the West Indies?

2   What is the name of the deepest point of the Caribbean
     Sea? It reaches a depth of 6,945 m/22,785 ft.

3   Who is credited with the discovery of the Caribbean
     Sea in 1493?

4   Which island along with Antigua makes up an
     independent Caribbean state?

5   Which Caribbean island became independent in 1978
     after 153 years of British colonial rule?

6   The Caribbean island Montserrat was devastated by
     volcanic eruption in 1997. To which group of islands
     does it belong?

7   Of which island is Fort-de-France the capital city?

8   Which port on the northwest coast of Cuba is also the
     island's capital?

9   Which is the largest of the Leeward Islands?

10   Give the name of the organization for economic and
     foreign policy coordination in the Caribbean.

Answers on page 174

1 From which country did Eritrea achieve independence in 1993?

2 At the mouth of which river does the city of Dublin stand?

3 What is the name of the mountainous peninsula of Mexico which stretches 1,300 km/800 mi south into the Pacific Ocean?

4 In which town of northern France is there a tapestry depicting the Norman invasion of England?

5 In which ocean are the Aleutian Islands?

6 Which British colony has a key and a castle on its flag?

7 On which Greek mountain can the sacred site of the Delphi oracle be seen?

8 In which American city will you find the Hale Observatories and the Mount Palomar telescope?

9 Where in Europe is the health resort and winter sports centre of Davos?

10 Which market town in Bavaria, Germany, is known for being the site of the first German concentration camp to be opened in 1935?

Answers on page 174

1 After whom was the Russian city of St Petersburg renamed in 1924?

2 Which large Russian island, the scene of a plane crash in 1983, is known to the Japanese as Karafuto?

3 How many constituent republics made up the former USSR?

4 What in Russia is a samovar?

5 Which river rises in the Smolensk region of Russia and flows south through Belarus and Ukraine to enter the Black Sea at Odessa?

6 What in Russia are Lagoda and Onega?

7 What is the name of the autonomous district of the Russian Federation which was part of the Krasnodar Province from 1936?

8 Which city, once capital of Russia in the Middle Ages, is now capital of Ukraine?

9 The world's deepest freshwater lake is situated in the Russian region of Siberia. What is it called?

10 Of which of the former Soviet republics is Yerevan the capital city?

Answers on page 174

1   Papua New Guinea occupies the eastern half of the
     island of New Guinea. Which country occupies the
     western half?

2   Which nation is made up of 844 islands, the largest
     being Viti Levu and Vanua Levu?

3   Of which waterway do the Bitter Lakes form a part?

4   In which European country is the region of Bohemia?

5   Which two ports offer the shortest ferry crossing
     between England and France?

6   Which region of the Adriatic coast, having the capital
     Split, has given its name to a popular breed of dog?

7   In which decade did Brasília replace Rio de Janeiro as
     the capital of Brazil?

8   40,000 of these Japanese swordsmen took part in the
     'Satsuma Rebellion' in 1877–78. By what name are
     they known?

9   What is the name of the submerged sandbank in the
     North Sea well known as a fishing region and as a
     shipping forecast area, its name means 'cod' in Dutch?

10   Which is the most northerly of the counties of the Irish
     Republic?

Answers on page 174

1   What was America's Cape Kennedy renamed in 1973?

2   Which cape is situated at the southwest tip of
       Portugal?

3   Give the name of the cape at the southern tip of Baja
       California, Mexico.

4   Which cape in Siberia marks the most northerly point
       on the continent of Asia?

5   Off the coast of which country is Cape Finisterre?

6   Which cape is situated at the most southerly point of
       South America?

7   This peninsula in Massachussetts, USA is 105 km/65
       mi long. What is its name?

8   Which cape is found at the northwest extremity of
       Scotland?

9   Originally known as the Cape of Storms, which cape
       can be found at the southwest tip of South Africa?

10   Which cape of France is the closest point to mainland
       Britain?

Answers on page 174

1   On which island off the British coast can you visit the 700 year-old Beaumaris Castle?

2   Which is the 'Volunteer State' of the USA?

3   What is the name of the port of Athens?

4   In which group of islands in the South Atlantic is Mount Pleasant airport?

5   Which group of islands in the north Atlantic have a Danish name meaning 'sheep islands'?

6   To which Swedish city is there a regular ferry service from Felixstowe in Suffolk?

7   In which city can you see the Brandenburg Gate?

8   To which Mediterranean island was Napoleon Bonaparte exiled in the years 1814–15?

9   The most easterly of the West Indies islands, its main industry is tourism and its capital city is Bridgetown. Which island country is this?

10   To which country do the Nicobar Islands belong?

Answers on page 174

1   Where is El Alamein, scene of a significant battle of
     World War II?

2   In which present-day country were the battles of
     Lexington and Concord fought in 1775?

3   One of the most famous naval battles in history was
     fought off Cape Trafalgar in 1815. Where is Cape
     Trafalgar?

4   Which well-known battle took place at Senlac Hill in
     southern England?

5   Which town in northern France was the site of the first
     major battle of the Hundred Years War in 1346?

6   Near which island group did the USA inflict heavy
     damage on the Japanese navy in a decisive battle of
     1942?

7   After which battle against Zulu forces in 1879 were
     eleven British soldiers awarded the Victoria Cross?

8   Near which river were General Custer and the 7th
     cavalry massacred by Sioux and Cheyennes in 1876?

9   In 1916 a famous sea battle was fought at Jutland by
     fleets commanded by Admiral John Jellicoe and
     Admiral Scheer. Where is Jutland?

10   Where did a famous battle take place in 490 BC, the
     name now being associated with the world of athletics?

Answers on page 175

1   Which island is separated from mainland Canada by the Juan de Fuca strait?

2   This nocturnal primate of Madagascar has an extended middle finger and is classified as an endangered species. What is it?

3   Which group of rocky islands off the coast of Northumberland, England, are a sanctuary for seals and seabirds, and also the scene of Grace Darling's rescue of shipwrecked sailors?

4   Of which province of southwest Iran is Shiraz the capital?

5   Which capital city stands at the confluence of the Danube and Sava rivers?

6   Which line of latitude lies 23.5° north of the Equator?

7   In which mountain range of New York State is the source of the Hudson River?

8   In which country is the Demerara River after which a type of brown sugar is named?

9   Which Dutch town on the Schie Canal has been famous since the 16th century for its distinctive blue and white pottery and porcelain?

10   Which US city in the Pacific northwest, where 'grunge' originated, is the headquarters of Boeing, the aircraft manufacturing company?

Answers on page 175

1   Which African republic lies on the Atlantic coast
     between Liberia and Guinea? Its capital is Freetown.

2   Which countries are divided along the 49th parallel?

3   Which large island is shared by the countries of
     Malaysia, Indonesia, and Brunei?

4   To which European country does the island of
     Greenland belong?

5   Which British colony was handed over to China in the
     summer of 1997?

6   Which small country close to the Adriatic Sea is
     entirely surrounded by Italian territory?

7   Which overseas département of France occupies a
     position between Suriname and Brazil on the northeast
     coast of South America?

8   Before its independence, which country did the
     Central American country of Belize belong to?

9   From which country did Libya become independent in
     1951?

10   To which country does the island of Corsica belong?

Answers on page 175

1 Which island is missing from this list: Kyushu, Shikoku, Hokkaido?

2 Of which Pakistani state is Lahore the capital?

3 Which English city did the Roman invaders call Deva?

4 In which country is the world's longest man-made canal?

5 Which Asian country has a name meaning 'Land of the free'?

6 Which is the longest river that flows into the English Channel?

7 Which state with its capital Portland, is sandwiched between California and Washington State on the Pacific coast of America?

8 What is the currency of Austria?

9 Which African capital city is the closest to the Equator?

10 In which country is the parliament known as the Folketing?

Answers on page 175

1   Which country uses the ringgit as its currency?

2   Which unit of currency is equal to 100 kopecks?

3   In which of the world's capital cities could you spend drachma?

4   Mauritius, Nepal, and the Seychelles all use which currency?

5   Name the coin, one hundred of which make one Spanish peseta.

6   In which two African countries is the kwacha the currency?

7   What is the currency of Denmark?

8   In which country did the austral replace the peso as the unit of currency in 1992?

9   What is the unit of currency in use in Libya, Tunisia, and Kuwait?

10 Which currency would you spend while visiting Montevideo, Bogotá, and Manila?

Answers on page 175

1   Of which group of British islands is Hugh Town the capital and major town?

2   Of which island is Nicosia the capital?

3   On which mountain are the carved heads of four American presidents to be seen?

4   Which is the sacred mountain of Japan?

5   In which country is Takliman Shamo the largest desert?

6   Which country's national airline is called Lufthansa?

7   Which city in Kansas was known as 'the cowboy capital of the world'?

8   What is the common name for the Malay Archipelago, used especially in a historical context?

9   Salem, Massachusetts, is associated with what famous trials?

10   Through which city in South Yorkshire, England, does the river Don flow?

Answers on page 175

1   What is the name of the famous bridge in Venice
        which links the Doge's Palace and the prison?

2   Which famous bridge now stands in Lake Havasu
        City, Arizona, USA?

3   Which bridge in Sydney, Australia has the world's
        longest concrete arch?

4   Which German river is spanned by the Zoo Bridge?

5   Completed in 1972, the Öland Island Bridge with a
        length of just under 6,100 m/20,000 ft is Europe's
        longest. In which country is it?

6   In which Italian city is the Rialto Bridge?

7   In which city could you cross the Jacques Cartier
        Bridge?

8   In which city is the Verrazzano Narrows Bridge?

9   What is the construction in northern Scotland which
        joins four of the Orkney Islands? It was put up in
        World War I and completed in 1943.

10   Which famous bridge spans the entrance to San
        Francisco Bay?

Answers on page 176

1   What is the Chinese name for the Spratly Islands in the South China Sea?

2   In which country is the Narmada Valley Project?

3   Hanoi is the capital of which communist country in the Far East?

4   Sapporo, Japan is a city that holds an annual snow festival in which giant figures are sculpted in the ice. Which prestigious international event was held there in 1972?

5   Which capital city is known to some of its citizens as Baile Atha Cliath?

6   Which Scottish village is supposedly named after the Dutchman John De Groot?

7   Which country's international car registration is ZA?

8   What is the collective name for Superior, Huron, Michigan, Erie, and Ontario?

9   In which European capital city is the Rijksmuseum art gallery?

10 What name is given to the calm regions of water close to the Equator?

Answers on page 176

1   In which country are the ruins of ancient Carthage?

2   Alexander the Great was king of which ancient region of Greece?

3   In which modern country are the ruins of Ephesus?

4   What did the ancient Romans call the area now known as France?

5   To which ancient civilization did the ruined city of Macchu Piccu belong?

6   Of which modern country is Mesopotamia now a part?

7   Which ancient civilization constructed two stone temples at Abu Simbel?

8   On which island did the Minoan civilization flourish in the Bronze Age?

9   Where did king Nebuchadnezzar II build his hanging gardens around the year 600 BC?

10 In which ancient Greek city, now a part of Turkey, was a tomb built for King Mausolus?

Answers on page 176

1 To which English county do the Farne Islands and Holy Island belong?

2 Which country's liberalization programme was halted by the invasion of 600,000 Soviet troops in 1968?

3 In which country are the towns of Salto and Pasyandú?

4 Which country has as its joint heads of state a Spaniard and a Frenchman?

5 Which group of more than 1,000 islands lies 644 km/400 mi southwest of Sri Lanka?

6 Where did Mount Pinatubo erupt in 1991?

7 What is another name for Ujung Padang, a port in Sulawesi, Indonesia?

8 Which is the only English island county?

9 Where are the Oesling and the Gutland?

10 What is the name for all citizens born and brought up in the Western Isles of Scotland?

Answers on page 176

1   What is the name of the Mediterranean coastline of Andalusia, southern Spain, stretching for nearly 300 km/190 mi from Algeciras to Almería?

2   What is the name of the Spanish dish of rice with vegetables and sea food?

3   What is the name of the light silk scarf worn over the head and shoulders (and often over a comb) by women in Spain?

4   Which is the longest river in Spain?

5   Which autonomous region of Spain includes the provinces of Granada, Seville, and Cádiz?

6   What is the capital city of the Spanish region of Aragon?

7   What is the name of the Mediterranean coastline of Alicante and Murcia provinces, eastern Spain?

8   What is the name of the Spanish parliament?

9   Which Spanish Balearic island, a popular destination for holiday makers has a capital called Palma?

10 Lanzarote is a popular holiday destination in which group of islands?

Answers on page 176

1 Which principality will become part of France if the reigning prince dies without producing a male heir?

2 Which country's currency is the guarani?

3 What is the capital of the republic of Haiti?

4 Which European country left the Commonwealth and declared itself a republic in 1949?

5 What is the name of the island country in the Caribbean, one of the Lesser Antilles, which gained independence in 1966?

6 Which island country in the north Atlantic Ocean is situated south of the Arctic Circle, between Greenland and Norway?

7 Which country in the west Pacific Ocean forms part of the archipelago of the Caroline Islands?

8 What in India are the Ghats?

9 What is the name of the triangular tableland in east India which stretches between the Vindhya Hills in the north, and the Western and Eastern Ghats in the south?

10 Which small country on the Gulf of Aden has borders with Somalia and Ethiopia?

Answers on page 176

1   The Brenner Pass in the Alps connects which two
     countries?

2   Which pass links the countries of Afghanistan and
     Pakistan?

3   Which of the great railway tunnels through the Alps
     was opened in 1882?

4   Which recently completed tunnel is sometimes
     referred to as the 'Chunnel'?

5   In which country are the Arlberg Pass and the Arlberg
     Tunnel?

6   In which mountain pass between Chile and Argentina
     can a huge statue of Christ be seen?

7   The Great Saint Bernard Pass connects Italy and
     Switzerland. Which country is connected to Italy by
     the Little Saint Bernard Pass?

8   What is the name of the pass through the Appalachian
     mountains of the USA situated near Middlesboro in
     Kentucky and discovered by Thomas Walker in 1750?

9   Which two of the four main islands of Japan are
     connected by the Seikan Tunnel?

10   Which two European countries are connected by the
     Simplon Tunnel?

Answers on page 177

1   The French national flag is called the Tricolor, meaning 'three colours'. What are the three colours?

2   Where in the world can you see two bridges linking one continent with another?

3   Which French city, an important wine centre, was under English rule for three centuries up until 1453?

4   What is the capital of Canada?

5   On which Japanese island is the port of Naha?

6   The West Bank of which river was occupied by Israel from 1967 and was the subject of a historic peace accord in 1993?

7   Which Indian river flows 560 km/350 mi from Chota Nagpur plateau in Bihar, through Bihar and the West Bengal states to join the Hooghly River 40 km/25 mi southwest of Calcutta?

8   Which English West Country spa city, called Aquae Sulis by the Romans, is famed for its hot springs, Gothic Abbey, and Roman remains?

9   In which South American country is Bio-Bio the longest river?

10   What is the name of the peninsula containing the countries of Spain and Portugal?

Answers on page 177

1   Which country presented the Statue of Liberty to the USA?

2   In which capital city could you visit the Bolshoi Theatre?

3   What is the name of the army of clay soldiers which can be seen at Xian, China?

4   In which English county can you visit Cheddar Gorge?

5   In which city is the Tivoli amusement park?

6   Which Swiss lakeside resort has an annual television festival whose top award is the Golden Rose?

7   In which European country is the original Legoland?

8   What is the major tourist attraction of the Texan city of San Antonio?

9   In which European capital city could you climb the Spanish Steps?

10 In which Californian city is the Disneyland amusement park?

Answers on page 177

1 Which range of mountains forms a natural barrier between Italy and the rest of Europe?

2 Ankara, in the Asian part of Turkey, is the country's capital. Which city in the European part did it replace?

3 What is the capital of Chile?

4 Which city and port on the Bay of Bengal was the only place in India attacked in World War I?

5 Which mountain range separates the Highlands of Scotland from the Lowlands?

6 What is the name of the deepest point in the world's oceans?

7 Which capital city of Europe stands on the river Aar?

8 In which English county is Tolpuddle, famous for the legend of the Tolpuddle Martyrs?

9 In which country is the historic oasis city of Marrakesh?

10 Where is the Greenwich Royal Observatory now located?

Answers on page 177

Waterfalls Around the World 125

1   The Sutherland Falls are 581 m/1,904 ft high. In which country are they?

2   On which river do the Victoria Falls stand?

3   Sherlock Holmes is supposed to have fallen to his death over the Reichenbach Falls. In which European country are they?

4   In which National Park of the USA are the Ribbon Falls?

5   The Gavarnie waterfall at 422 m/1,384 ft is one of the highest falls in Europe. In which country is it?

6   Which famous waterfalls were discovered by David Livingstone in 1855?

7   The Tugela Falls in South Africa, with a total drop of 947 m/3,110 ft, consists of how many individual falls?

8   Which are the world's greatest waterfalls in terms of volume of water passing over them?

9   In the Niagara Falls, which island separates the Canadian (or Horseshoe) Falls and the American Falls?

10   In which country is the highest waterfall in the world, the Angel Falls, at 978 m/3,210 ft?

Answers on page 177

1   Which city in Provence has a 12th-century bridge on which everyone danced, according to an old French song?

2   What is the name of the nine Portuguese islands in the Atlantic Ocean which are actually volcanic peaks?

3   Which country was defeated by the USSR in the 'Winter War' of 1939?

4   What is the capital of Belarus?

5   The dong is which country's currency unit?

6   In which Buckinghamshire new town, England, does the Open University have its headquarters?

7   Which country is composed of over 7,000 islands including Mindoro, Luzon, Minanao, and Palawan?

8   What is the name for Wales in the Welsh language?

9   In which US city is O'Hare international airport?

10   Vanuatu became independent in 1980. By what name was it known before independence?

Answers on page 177

1   What is the German name for Bavaria, a region of Germany?

2   On which river does the port of Hamburg stand?

3   In German public places you may see a sign saying 'Rauchen verboten'. What does this mean?

4   After the reunification of East and West Germany, who won a resounding victory as the first chancellor in 1990?

5   Which is the second-largest state of Germany after Bavaria?

6   In which year was the Berlin Wall constructed?

7   In which valley in Germany is the major concentration of industry and the most densely populated region?

8   Which is the highest mountain in Germany?

9   Of which German region is Munich the capital?

10   By what name is the mountainous region of coniferous forest in Baden-Württemberg, western Germany usually known?

Answers on page 178

1   Which French river flows into the sea at St Nazaire and is famous for its châteaux?

2   Which historic city is Italy's main port?

3   Which range of mountains extends some 65 km/40 mi along the border of Poland and the Slovak Republic?

4   What is the capital of Somalia?

5   Which part of Norway is the most northerly part of Europe?

6   What is the name of the lake on the frontier between Albania and the Former Yugoslav Republic of Macedonia?

7   Which district of London gave its name to the prime meridian?

8   What is the present name of the capital city that used to be known as Edo?

9   Of which mountainous country is Vaduz the capital city?

10   Which African country was formerly known as Bechuanaland?

Answers on page 178

1   Which Central American country's capital is
     Tegucigalpa?

2   Which explorer landed in what is now the West Indies
     in 1492?

3   The currency is the cordoba, the language is Spanish
     and the capital is Managua. Which country is this?

4   Which of the countries of Central America was
     formerly known as British Honduras?

5   In which country is the naval base of Puerto Barrios?

6   In which Central American country was there conflict
     between the ruling Sandinista government and the US-
     backed Contra rebels?

7   Which is the smallest and most densely populated of
     the countries of Central America?

8   The majority of the population of which country live
     in an area known as the Meseta Central, a broad
     plateau in the centre of the country?

9   Which river, 965 km/600 mi long, forms part of the
     border between Guatemala and Mexico?

10   Which coastal region of Nicaragua and Honduras has
     the same name as a type of insect?

Answers on page 178

1   In which country are the Vosges mountains?

2   Which river forms a part of the border between the English counties of Norfolk and Suffolk?

3   Innsbruck in Austria stands on the river Inn. Of which major river is this a tributary?

4   What is the official language of Ghana?

5   On which French river is the world's first successful tidal power station?

6   What is the capital of Saudi Arabia?

7   Which English city was known as Eboracum to the Romans?

8   Which metal is mined at the Canadian town of Sudbury?

9   On which continent is Paramaribo a capital city?

10   Which expanse of sea near the Orkney Islands was used as a base by the Royal Navy until 1957?

Answers on page 178

1   Which South African city, the largest in the country, is the centre for the gold-mining industry?

2   Which landlocked country is an enclave within the country of South Africa?

3   One of the two official languages of South Africa is Afrikaans – what is the other?

4   Which is the major mountain range of South Africa?

5   Which river flows along part of the South African border with both Botswana and Zaire?

6   What is the name of the diamond-mining town situated 153 km/95 mi northwest of Bloemfontein?

7   Which year saw the lifting of the ban on the African National Congress (ANC) and the release from prison of Nelson Mandela?

8   Which city is the judicial capital of South Africa?

9   It is the capital of the North West Province, and a casino resort. By what name is it commonly known?

10   South Africa is the world's largest producer of which precious metal?

Answers on page 178

1   The capital cities of Guyana, Penang in Malaysia, and the Cayman Islands share the same name. What is it?

2   What is the French name for Burgundy, a region of eastern France?

3   Which peninsula at the northern end of the Red Sea links Africa with southwest Asia?

4   Which long river said to be the most polluted in Europe has its source in Switzerland and its mouth at the North Sea in the Netherlands?

5   Which Russian city changed its name back to the original St Petersburg after the fall of the USSR?

6   Which sea, lapping at the coast of northeast Africa, is actually a submerged section of the Great Rift Valley?

7   What is the nationality of somebody born on the Madeira Islands?

8   Which resort in northern France lies at the mouth of the river Canche and was fashionable in the 1920s and 1930s?

9   What is the capital of Mauritius?

10   Which Asian country with an area over six times that of the UK only has a population of 2.3 million people?

Answers on page 178

Name the Country   133

Identify the country as quickly as possible from the clues given:

1 **a** This is a country in northern Europe of which 25% is covered by forest.

  b Harald V became king in 1991 on the death of his father Olav.

  c Stavanger and Trondtheim are two of the major towns.

2 **a** This is a republic of northwest Africa which achieved independence from France in 1960.

  b The two official languages are French and Arabic; the capital was formerly known as Fort Lamy.

  c It lies due south of Libya.

3 **a** This is a Central American republic with a population of just over 3 million and major exports including coffee, bananas, sugar, and cocoa.

  b Bordered to the north by Nicaragua and to the south by Panama, one of the major ports is Puntarenas.

  c The Spanish name of the country means 'rich coast' in English.

4 **a** A socialist republic of Asia, the Mekong delta is found here.

  b The country was divided in two along the 17th parallel in 1954 and reunited in 1976.

  c Ho Chi Minh City, formerly Saigon, is one of the major ports in this country.

5 **a** This is a country of South America of which 27% is covered by the Andes mountains.

  b Situated on the northwest coast of South America, this country has borders with Ecuador and Colombia to the north, and with Chile and Bolivia to the south.

  c The Inca civilization flourished in this country.

Answers on page 179

6 a This is a European sovereign state with an area of just 1.95 sq km/0.75 sq mi.

   b The economy is almost totally dependent on tourism and gambling.

   c Situated on the Mediterranean Sea, a famous annual Grand Prix is held on the streets of its main resort.

7 a This island country in the Indian Ocean is situated approximately 1,200 km/746 mi east of Kenya.

   b At various times since 1744 it had been a French and British colony. It became independent in 1976 under the presidency of James Malchan.

   c Although the country consists of over 100 islands over 90% of the population live on the major island Mahè.

8 a This is a landlocked mountainous country of central Europe consisting of nine provinces.

   b The country became independent in 1955 after being occupied by allied forces from the end of World War II.

   c Salzburg, the birthplace of Mozart, is in this country.

9 a This is an Asian country which was known by another name until 1989; over 50% of its territory is covered in rainforest.

   b The capital city is now called Yangon and the Chidwin and Irrawaddy rivers are found here.

   c It was known until 1989 as Burma.

10 a Officially known as a dominion, this country became independent within the British Commonwealth in 1947.

    b The country is made up of a number of islands including Chatham Island and Stewart Island.

    c The capital city is named after one of England's most famous soldiers and prime ministers.

Answers on page 179

1   In which country do 100 piastres make one pound?

2   Which is the smallest country in Africa?

3   Which island lies to the north of Australia across the Torres Strait?

4   What is the capital of Morocco?

5   On which river does Belfast stand?

6   In which country is the Simpson Desert?

7   Which country claims the Antarctic territory of Queen Maud Land?

8   What is the nationality of someone born in the city of Lima?

9   What is the name of the thin stretch of coastal land occupied by Israel during the Six-Day War of 1967?

10   Which is the most important of the islands of Indonesia, on which you will find the capital Jakarta?

Answers on page 179

1   Who came to prominence when he overthrew the dictator Fulgencio Batista in 1959?

2   In which country did Papa Doc and Baby Doc Duvalier have a reign of terror?

3   Which country was ruled for forty years by the dictator Antonio Salazar?

4   Israel was proclaimed an independent state in 1948. Who was its prime minister from then until 1963?

5   In which country did Grand Duke Jean become head of state in 1964?

6   The world's first woman prime minister was appointed by which island nation in 1960?

7   Of which state was Bill Clinton governor before becoming president of the USA?

8   In which country did President Mubarak come to power in 1981 after the assassination of Anwar Sadat, to be re-elected in 1987 and 1993?

9   Where was Nelson Mandela held prisoner for 27 years?

10   In which country did Paul Keating become prime minister in 1992?

Answers on page 179

1   Which narrow stretch of water about 80 km/50 mi long, connects the Aegean Sea to the Sea of Marmara?

2   In which capital city are the remains of the Pantheon and the Forum?

3   What is the name of the large arm of the Mediterranean Sea, lying NW to SE between the Italian and the Balkan peninsulas?

4   Which European city is the highest capital in Europe, on an elevated plateau 655 m/2,183 ft above sea level?

5   Godthaab, with a small population of only 12,200, is the capital and largest town on which island, said to be the largest in the world?

6   Which region in the Caucasus is on the border between Russia and Georgia?

7   What was the name given to the continents of the eastern hemisphere, so called because they were familiar to Europeans before the Americas?

8   At which site 5 km/3 mi southeast of Heraklion, on Crete, is there an excavated palace of the Minoan civilization?

9   In which Soviet republic was the space launch site, the Baikonur Cosmodrome, built?

10   Which became the 50th state of the USA in 1959?

Answers on page 179

1 Which city in Italy flourished as a centre of art from the 13th to the 16th centuries, producing highly decorative art as in *The Crucifixion* by Giovanni di Paolo?

2 In which city is the world famous Hermitage museum?

3 In which city would you find Leonardo's *Last Supper*?

4 In which art gallery can you see Leonardo's world famous Mona Lisa?

5 What nationality was the famous surrealist Salvador Dali?

6 Which Italian city was the favourite subject of the artist Canaletto?

7 By what name was the Greek artist Doménikos Theotokopoulos better known?

8 Who painted a famous picture of the Spanish town of Guernica, devastated by bombing during the Spanish Civil War?

9 Which city in northern Italy where Leonardo and Michaelangelo lived is a cultural and tourist centre because of its art and architecture?

10 On which Greek island was a famous sculpture without arms found in 1820?

Answers on page 179

1   What is the name of the coastal desert region in
     Namibia between the Kalahari Desert and the Atlantic
     Ocean?

2   Where did Louis and Mary Leakey find prehistoric
     stone tools in the 1930s?

3   Which Arab city on the Mediterranean has almost the
     same name as the country of which it is capital?

4   Mayotte is part of which island state off Africa's east
     coast?

5   Which former Dutch colony became independent in
     1975 as Suriname?

6   Which Russian seaport is the largest within the Arctic
     circle, with a population of 432,000?

7   The Rock of Gibraltar is a British dependency on a
     promontory on the coast of which country?

8   Arabic and which other language are the official
     languages of Chad?

9   What is the capital of Nepal?

10   In which country are the ruins of the great temple of
     Angkor Wat?

Answers on page 179

1   In which Spanish town does the annual running of the bulls take place?

2   In Tibet, what are hard slabs of tea used as before being brewed?

3   Which Brazilian city is noted for its colourful annual carnival?

4   Which British city holds an annual Goose Fair?

5   Friesland is an area of the Netherlands where in very cold winters they hold the Elftstedentocht, a race by canal through 11 towns. What do they race with?

6   In which German town is a passion play held every 10 years?

7   The Oktoberfest is an annual German festival celebrating what?

8   What is the name of the traditional war dance performed by the Maoris of New Zealand?

9   Where in Britain is the tradition of 'Up-Helly-Aa' practised?

10   Which city of Louisiana, USA, is famed for its annual Mardi Gras celebrations?

Answers on page 180

1   Which country is divided in two just north of the 38th parallel?

2   Which country does Iberian airlines operate from?

3   Which crater in the Tanzanian section of the Great Rift Valley is notable for its large numbers of wildebeest, gazelle, and zebra?

4   What, until 1975, was the name of the Bight of Bonny off the west African coast?

5   On which peninsula do the countries of Turkey, Bulgaria, and Albania lie?

6   Which country has the highest density of sheep in the world?

7   What is the capital of Libya?

8   What is the capital city of Pakistan?

9   Which is the largest lake in the Lake District and also in England?

10 On which of the Japanese islands does Mount Fujiyama stand?

Answers on page 180

1   What is the name of the highest peak in the Antarctic?

2   What is the name of the national park created in 1980
     from a vast wilderness area of Alaska including the
     Valley of Ten Thousand Smokes?

3   This dry, uninhabited desert region of the Arabian
     peninsula has a name which translates as 'empty
     quarter'. What is its Arabic name?

4   What name is given to the great wilderness area of
     central Australia?

5   What name is given to the treeless area between the ice
     cap and the tree line in arctic regions?

6   What is the name of the sparsely inhabited region of
     Canada between the Mackenzie River basin and Hudson
     Bay?

7   What is the name for the barren region of Europe
     crossing the borders of Norway, Sweden, Finland, and
     Russia, within the Arctic Circle?

8   Which area of Russia, covering over 70% of the country
     from the Urals to the Pacific, is known for its long,
     extremely cold winters?

9   On which gulf of the Arctic Ocean does Arkhangelsk
     stand?

10   What is the name of the geographical depression
     225 km/140 mi long and 85 m/280 ft below sea level
     in southeast California, USA?

Answers on page 180

1   Belgium, West Germany, France, Italy, and Luxembourg were five of the six original countries of the European Community. Which was the sixth?

2   Which country left the British Commonwealth in 1971?

3   Which African country was formerly known as Nyasaland?

4   Of which island is St Peter Port the major town?

5   Which geographical projection was constituted by Somalia and adjacent territories?

6   What is the nationality of someone born in Alice Springs?

7   In which northern European country is Lake Vanern?

8   What is the capital of Iran?

9   What is the name of the strait lying between Iceland and Greenland?

10   Which is the longest river in Scotland?

Answers on page 180

1. Which Pacific state is the most populated state of the USA with nearly 30 million inhabitants?

2. Which is the most populated country on earth?

3. The fifth largest country in Africa, it only has a population density of three people per sq km and a total population of slightly over 5 million. Which country is this?

4. Which Asian republic and former British colony has almost 3 million people living in an area of only 622 sq km/240 sq mi?

5. The state of Alaska ranks first in the states of the USA according to size. Where does it rank according to population?

6. Which principality has a population of only 31,000 but a population density of 31,349 people per sq km (1994)?

7. Which is the second most populated city of England after London?

8. Which is the only state in the world with a zero birth rate?

9. Although New Delhi is the capital city of India it is not the most populated city in the country – which is?

10. Which is the most densely populated country in Europe after the principality of Monaco?

Answers on page 180

1   What is the major tributary of the Mississippi River?

2   What is the alternate name of Lake Turkana, a lake of northwest Kenya in the Great Rift Valley?

3   How many yellow stars are there on the national flag of China?

4   In which state of the USA is the port of Mobile?

5   Which is the second largest city of Mexico?

6   What is the southernmost cape in Africa?

7   Where in the United Kingdom are the Mourne Mountains?

8   Which is the most southerly state of the USA?

9   Windhoek is the capital of which African country?

10   Which borough of New York City, USA, occupies the southwest end of Long Island?

Answers on page 180

1   What is the name of the brightly coloured wraparound skirt worn by men and women in Malaysia and the Pacific islands?

2   What is the name of the blanket-like cloak with a hole for the head worn in Spanish-American countries?

3   Which type of warm hooded coat is named after a town in Belgium?

4   What is the name of the pouch traditionally worn at the front of a kilt?

5   Where in the world do men wear traditional dress known as dhoti?

6   Which city of Morocco has given its name to a type of hat?

7   What is the name of the short leather trousers worn by men in Bavaria?

8   On which part of the body do people in some European countries wear sabots?

9   What is the name of the veil worn by Muslim women to cover the face in public?

10   Which type of fur hat is named after a Russian city on the Volga delta?

Answers on page 181

1   On which river does Moscow stand?

2   What is the former name of Lake Mobutu in central
     Africa?

3   What name is given to the peninsula comprising part
     of Thailand, western Malaysia, and Singapore?

4   What is the nationality of someone born in Pretoria?

5   On which river does the Russian city of St Petersburg
     stand?

6   For the manufacture of what is the German town of
     Meissen renowned?

7   What is separated from mainland Wales by the Menai
     straits?

8   Which Pennsylvanian city has a name which means
     'city of brotherly love'?

9   The port of Tobruk was the scene of heavy fighting
     during World War II. In which north African country
     is it?

10   On which South Atlantic island did Napoleon
     Bonaparte die in 1821?

Answers on page 181

1   Which huge African dam stands on the
     Zambia–Zimbabwe border?

2   The world's longest dam stands on the Mahanadi
     River in India. How long is it to the nearest mile or
     kilometre?

3   Which dam on the Columbia River, USA supports the
     waters of Franklin D Roosevelt Lake?

4   Tehri and Kishau are the names of the two largest
     dams in which country?

5   Which shallow freshwater lake of the Netherlands was
     created by the construction of two dams in 1932?

6   In which country is the Aswan High Dam?

7   The Grand Dixence Dam with a height of 285 m/935 ft
     is the highest dam in Europe. In which country is it?

8   Which important dam on the Colorado River was
     formerly known as the Boulder Dam?

9   On which African river can you see the Kariba Dam?

10   The construction of which dam necessitated the
     removal and reconstruction of the ancient temples of
     Abu Simbel?

Answers on page 181

1   On which Japanese city was the second atomic bomb
     dropped during World War II?

2   Which arid plateau in Spain was the setting for the
     novel *Don Quixote*?

3   Which Swiss city on the north shore of Lake Geneva is
     the capital of the canton of Vaud?

4   Which historic English city shares its name with the
     state capital of Nebraska?

5   Of which country are the Azores a possession?

6   Which region occupies the so called 'toe' of Italy?

7   Three quarters of which continent lies within the
     tropics?

8   What is the official language of Argentina?

9   Off the coast of which country is Kangaroo Island?

10   In which country is the largest part of the Kalahari
     desert?

Answers on page 181

1   In which US range of hills is Mount Rushmore?

2   In which English county are the Quantock Hills?

3   In which range of hills is the source of the river Thames?

4   Where would you find seven hills called Aventine, Capitoline, Esquiline, Quirinal, Caelian, Viminal, and Palatine?

5   Which major river rises in the Valdai hills northwest of Moscow?

6   Where did the first major battle of the American War of Independence take place in 1775?

7   Of which range of English hills is Coombe Hill near Wendover, Buckinghamshire, the highest point?

8   In which Asian country are the Chin Hills situated?

9   At the foot of which hill was the biblical Garden of Gethsemane?

10   On which Italian hill did allied bombers destroy a Benedictine monastery in 1944?

Answers on page 181

1   Which small island situated between the Shetlands and the Orkneys is known for its distinctive knitted sweaters?

2   Which state across the Hudson River from New York is the most densely populated state in the USA with almost 1,000 people per square mile?

3   Which is Africa's most populated city?

4   Of which country was Kenneth Kaunda the first president?

5   What is the nationality of somebody born on the island of Lanzarote?

6   What is the capital of Oman?

7   What is the name of the forested glen of great scenic beauty lying between the lochs Katrine and Achray in Scotland's central region?

8   In which state of the USA is Dodge City, famed as a frontier town in wild west days?

9   Which important shipping channel lies between Scotland and the Orkney Islands?

10   Which country's airline is KLM?

Answers on page 181

ANSWERS

1 Capital Cities

1 Nigeria
2 Addis Ababa
3 Victoria
4 Nepal
5 Lhasa
6 Washington DC
7 Uttar Pradesh
8 Stockholm
9 Brasília
10 Edwin Lutyens

2 General Knowledge

1 Tundra
2 A musical instrument
3 Notre Dame Cathedral
4 Khartoum
5 Spain
6 Limburger
7 The eagle
8 China
9 Macao
10 Mahé

3 Food Around the World

1 Soya
2 Bortsch
3 Pickled cabbage
4 Hungary
5 China
6 Austria
7 Switzerland
8 Greece
9 Grape
10 Lübeck

4 General Knowledge

1 Australia
2 Cape of Good Hope
3 A type of boat
4 Dinar
5 Charleston
6 Ghana
7 Norwegian – led by Roald Amundsen
8 Bell tower or campanile
9 Bayreuth
10 Demerara

5 Australasia

1 Ayers Rock
2 New Guinea
3 Sydney
4 Suva
5 Alice Springs
6 Barossa Valley
7 Koala
8 Coral Sea
9 Nullabor Plain
10 Gulf of Carpentaria

6 General Knowledge

1 *Torino*
2 Byzantium and Constantinople
3 Turkey
4 Diamonds
5 Honshu
6 Corsica
7 Volcanoes
8 Lambada
9 Trans-Siberian railway
10 Akrotiri

7   Foreign Names

1 English Channel
2 Greece
3 Dodecanese
4 *Bharat*
5 *Moskva*
6 Tierra del Fuego
7 Lake Constance
8 Danube
9 Mount Everest
10 Amazon – from *Amassona*

8   General Knowledge

1 Muscadet
2 North Yorkshire
3 New England
4 Morocco
5 Falkland Islands
6 Geneva
7 Organization of African Unity (OAU)
8 Lake Superior
9 Ascension
10 A Himalayan mountain

9   Animals Around the World

1 Yak
2 Camargue
3 Vienna
4 Butterfly
5 Labrador
6 Australia
7 Canary Islands – from Latin *canis*
8 Mexico
9 Galapagos Islands
10 Orangutan

10   General Knowledge

1 Krajina
2 Iceland
3 Adige
4 Camembert
5 Aletsch
6 New Hebrides
7 Asia
8 New York
9 Valparaíso
10 Pennines

11   Islands

1 Indonesia
2 Hispaniola
3 Rhodes
4 Comoros
5 Kharg Island
6 Surtsey
7 Tristan da Cunha
8 Sri Lanka
9 Falklands
10 Malta

12   General Knowledge

1 Australia
2 Cairo
3 Drumlin
4 Basque
5 David Livingstone
6 Sydney
7 Assam
8 League of Arab States, or Arab League
9 Caspian Sea
10 Abu Dhabi

13   Places of Worship

1 Istanbul
2 Barcelona
3 Moscow – in Red Square
4 Venice
5 Santiago de Compostela
6 Myanmar, formerly Burma
7 Montmartre
8 Mont St Michel
9 Casablanca
10 Amritsar

14   General Knowledge

1 Jumna
2 Oklahoma
3 Charles I
4 Mecca
5 Montréal
6 Australia
7 Monaco
8 Arctic Ocean
9 Lourdes
10 Arran

15   Holiday Destinations

1 Bali
2 Jamaica
3 Tenerife
4 Algarve
5 Costa Blanca
6 Côte d'Azur
7 Engadine
8 Mexico
9 Mustique
10 Rio de Janeiro

16   General Knowledge

1 Aix-la-Chapelle
2 Windy City
3 Nepal
4 New Zealand
5 Mauritius
6 Klondike
7 Cornwall
8 Corfu
9 Tigris
10 Brussels

17 Lakes Around the World

1 Lake Nicaragua
2 Lake Victoria
3 Lake Como
4 Lake Ontario
5 Hungary
6 Lake Titicaca
7 Lake Chad
8 Lake Michigan
9 The Lake District
10 Finland

18   General Knowledge

1 Bolivia and Peru
2 Western Samoa
3 South Africa
4 Transylvania
5 A crater found at the summit of a volcano
6 Switzerland
7 The Rockies
8 Tasmania
9 Cuba
10 Lindisfarne

19 Name the City

1 Khartoum
2 Florence
3 Bombay
4 Buenos Aires
5 Melbourne
6 Chicago
7 Bonn
8 Cape Town
9 Shanghai
10 Copenhagen

20 General Knowledge

1 Galapagos Islands
2 Denmark
3 Ikebana
4 Missouri
5 Melbourne
6 Confederation of Independent
   States (CIS)
7 Salzburg
8 Voodoo
9 Netherlands
10 Arlington

21 World Ports

1 Fremantle
2 Lebanon
3 Vladivostok
4 Bandar Shah
5 Alexandria
6 Honduras
7 Anchorage
8 Jaffa
9 Tanzania
10 Durban

22 General Knowledge

1 Jordan
2 Illinois
3 The Afars and the Issas
4 Ajaccio
5 Ukraine
6 Beijing
7 Damaraland
8 Acre
9 Assam
10 Falkland Islands

23 Africa

1 Tanzania
2 Sudan
3 Mali
4 Kharga
5 Cahora Bassa
6 The Gambia
7 Zambezi
8 Aouzu Strip
9 Atlas Mountains
10 Algeria

24 General Knowledge

1 European Union (EU)
2 Lusitania
3 Yemen
4 Apollo
5 Karakorum
6 Luzon
7 Borneo
8 *Mani puliti*
9 By peat digging
10 Hebrew and Arabic

25   Canada

1 Klondike
2 Quèbec
3 Acadia
4 Toronto
5 Newfoundland
6 Nova Scotia
7 Lake Ontario
8 Kingston
9 Vancouver
10 Alberta

26   General Knowledge

1 Liberia
2 Sir Francis Chichester
3 Alabama
4 Ecuador
5 Spanish and Quechna
6 Jute
7 Winds
8 Norway
9 Islam
10 Congress

27   Mountain Ranges

1 Atlas Mountains
2 Sierra Nevada
3 Cairngorms
4 Pyrenees
5 Cèvennes
6 Swartberg Mountains
7 South Africa
8 Andes
9 Greece
10 Cascade Range

28   General Knowledge

1 Carpets
2 Rio de Janeiro
3 Moselle
4 Fjords
5 Denmark
6 River Po
7 Cape Byron
8 Barrow Island
9 Alberta
10 Cyclades

29   Italy

1 Piedmont
2 Dante Alighieri
3 Umbria
4 Assisi
5 Dolomites
6 Mezzogiorno
7 Liguria
8 Larderello
9 Capri
10 Avernus

30   General Knowledge

1 Asia Minor
2 Navarre
3 Africa
4 Switzerland
5 Laughing jackass
6 Atlantic Ocean
7 Bay of Campeche
8 New Zealand
9 Iron
10 Shining Path

31   Flags

1. Red
2. Maple leaf
3. Cyprus
4. Six
5. Blue and white
6. Nepal
7. USA
8. New Zealand
9. Blue
10. Lebanon

32   General Knowledge

1. Bread
2. Madeira Islands
3. Siam
4. Strasbourg
5. Padua
6. Madagascar
7. Inkatha Freedom Party (IFP)
8. Ganges
9. New York Harbor
10. Vancouver

33   Drinks Around
the World

1. India
2. Sicily
3. Cognac
4. Cherry
5. Ouzo
6. Chianti
7. Poteen
8. Red wine
9. California
10. Mokha or Mocha

34   General Knowledge

1. European Economic Community or EEC (modern European Union or EU)
2. Apartheid
3. Abadan
4. Argentina
5. Arno
6. Croissants
7. Boston – he was known as the 'Boston strangler'
8. Sikhism
9. Québec
10. Desert Storm

35   Political Systems
Around the World

1. Angola
2. Absolutism
3. Autocracy
4. USA
5. China
6. Norway
7. Junta
8. Inkatha Freedom Party (IFP)
9. Dáil Éireann
10. Argentina

36   General Knowledge

1. Aduwa
2. Danzig
3. Granada
4. Abilene
5. Nigeria
6. Orinoco
7. Apennines
8. White
9. Frankfurter
10. Seoul

37 South America

1 Paraguay or Bolivia
2 Colombia
3 Gauchos
4 Tierra del Fuego
5 Sugar Loaf Mountain
6 Atacama Desert
7 Beagle Channel
8 Altiplano
9 Ecuador
10 Lake Titicaca

38 General Knowledge

1 The Faroes
2 Vltava
3 1990
4 Lamb
5 Burma
6 Virginia
7 King Zog
8 Aberystwyth
9 Halloween
10 Bristol

39 The Middle East

1 Iran
2 Bahrain
3 The Levant
4 Petra
5 Mesopotamia
6 Masirah Island
7 Orontes
8 Egypt
9 Beirut
10 River Jordan

40 General Knowledge

1 'Hello'
2 Death Valley
3 Western Australia
4 Rio de Janeiro
5 Longchamp
6 Antarctica
7 Proportional representation
8 Isle of Man
9 Hirohito
10 Détente

41 World Exploration

1 Robert O'Hara Burke and William Wills
2 Antarctic
3 Greenland
4 Hispaniola
5 Columbus
6 Lake Tanganyika
7 New Britain
8 Christmas Island
9 Angel Falls, Venezuela
10 Hawaii

42 General Knowledge

1 Uganda
2 Netherlands
3 Colombia
4 Northwest Passage
5 Japan
6 Bahamas
7 Queen Victoria
8 Wyoming
9 Cheviot Hills
10 Calvados

43   Rivers Around the World

1 Danube
2 River Plate
3 Tibet
4 Mekong
5 Orinoco
6 St Lawrence
7 Norway
8 New Zealand
9 Colorado River
10 Volga

44   General Knowledge

1 Australian Aborigines
2 The tablecloth
3 La Paz
4 A Chinese province
5 Crete
6 Monaco
7 Golden Gate
8 Indian Ocean
9 New York
10 Miami

45   Japan

1 Iwo Jima
2 Saki
3 A type of porcelain
4 Kamikaze
5 Sapporo
6 Kawasaki
7 Growing miniature trees
8 Ritual suicide
9 Sumo wrestling
10 Okinawa

46   General Knowledge

1 Belfast
2 Florida
3 Nelson Mandela
4 Black Forest
5 Albertville
6 Jordan
7 Hiroshima
8 Nottinghamshire
9 Chicago
10 Caspian Sea

47   Bays and Gulfs Around the World

1 Botany Bay
2 The Indian Ocean
3 Bay of Biscay
4 Chesapeake Bay
5 Bay of Pigs
6 New Zealand
7 Jervis Bay
8 Botany Bay
9 Gulf of Mexico
10 Arabian Gulf

48   General Knowledge

1 Danube
2 Australia
3 Ionian Sea
4 Australian rules
5 Jacques Chirac
6 Mountain range
7 Inuit
8 Your birthday
9 Scilly Isles
10 Alaska Highway

1 Strasbourg
2 French Riviera
3 Mont Blanc
4 Mustard
5 Limoges
6 Lascaux
7 Marne
8 Pas-de-Calais
9 Loire
10 Marseille

50 General Knowledge

1 Blue
2 Colorado River
3 Chablis
4 The Dead Sea
5 Shetland Islands
6 1956
7 Dayton
8 Israel
9 Franklin D Roosevelt – 12 years
10 Yellow River

51 Europe

1 Helsinki
2 Rhine and Rhône
3 Budapest
4 Euratom
5 Croatia
6 Austria
7 Treaty of Rome
8 Gdańsk
9 Denmark and Sweden
10 Athos

1 Igneous
2 Achill Island
3 Black Hills
4 Memphis
5 Uruguay
6 Hill figures
7 Alaska
8 Haiti
9 Paul Klee
10 Retsina

53 Neighbouring Countries

1 Yemen
2 Venezuela
3 Austria
4 Burkina Faso
5 Germany
6 Vietnam
7 Central African Republic
8 Nicaragua
9 Jordan
10 Liechtenstein

54 General Knowledge

1 Le Mans
2 Aspen
3 Olney
4 Knesset
5 Alaska
6 Europe and Asia
7 Aegean Sea – from Aegeus
8 Boris Yeltsin
9 Fingal's Cave
10 Finland

55   What's in a Name?

1 George Bass – Bass Strait
2 Amerigo Vespucci
3 Simón Bolívar (Bartholdi)
4 George Everest
5 Pittsburgh
6 Falkland Islands
7 Darwin
8 James Monroe – Monrovia
9 Victoria
10 Adelaide

56   General Knowledge

1 Tangier
2 Turkey
3 Estonia
4 Alps
5 Argentina
6 Alcatraz
7 Florida
8 Medina
9 Vasco da Gama
10 North Atlantic Treaty
Organization (NATO)

57   Famous Buildings Around the World

1 Elysèe Palace
2 Taj Mahal
3 Derbyshire
4 The White House
5 New York
6 Arc de Triomphe
7 Chicago
8 Athens
9 Buckingham Palace
10 Sydney Opera House

58   General Knowledge

1 Somalia
2 Lake Victoria
3 Harare
4 Québec
5 Wyoming
6 Brunei
7 Andalusia
8 Beaches
9 Illegally distilled alcohol
10 Origami

59   USA

1 Florida Keys
2 Manhattan
3 Andy Warhol
4 Boston
5 Old Faithful
6 Martin's Hundred
7 Bonneville Salt Flats
8 Missouri
9 Nevada
10 Connecticut

60   General Knowledge

1 Varanasi – formerly Benares
2 Aquavit
3 Mull
4 Chagos
5 Burkina Faso
6 Canada
7 Christchurch
8 Cinque Ports
9 Tuvalu
10 Entebbe

61 Nicknames Around the World

1 Denver
2 Venice
3 Silicon Valley
4 Aberdeen
5 Lhasa in Tibet
6 Paris
7 Edinburgh
8 Bruges
9 Albufeira
10 Kara Sea

62 General Knowledge

1 Hamelin
2 North American Native Americans
3 Brazil
4 Inupiaq
5 Germany
6 Hindu
7 Capri
8 Chihuahua
9 Bangladesh
10 Clare

63 Seas and Oceans Around the World

1 Antarctica
2 Coral Sea
3 Yellow Sea
4 Black Sea
5 Baltic Sea
6 Dead Sea
7 Atlantic
8 Aral Sea
9 Sargasso Sea
10 Arctic Ocean

64 General Knowledge

1 São Paulo
2 Zealand
3 Florence
4 Louis XIV
5 Beaufort Sea
6 Detroit
7 Red Crescent
8 Brunei
9 Gulf of California
10 Camargue

65 Asia

1 Mongolia
2 Israel
3 Celebes
4 Colombo
5 Laos
6 New Guinea
7 Seven
8 Tibet
9 Borneo
10 Indonesia

66 General Knowledge

1 Broken Hill
2 Bruges
3 Tanganyika
4 Bulawayo
5 Istanbul
6 Cagliari
7 Jordan
8 Frank Lloyd Wright
9 Alderney
10 Cumbria

67   Mountains Around the World

1 K2, also known as Chogori or Mount Godwin-Austen
2 Cape Town
3 Garfield Mountain
4 Ben Nevis
5 Olympus
6 Atlas Mountains
7 Mount Elbrus
8 Eiger
9 Mount McKinley
10 The Matterhorn

68   General Knowledge

1 Communism
2 Australia
3 Peru
4 Venice – by gondoliers
5 Black Forest Gateau
6 Devil's Island
7 Sydney Opera House
8 Big Apple – New York City
9 Québec
10 Stanley Falls

69   Former Names

1 Gibraltar
2 Ghana
3 Kinshasa
4 Saigon
5 Persia
6 Ethiopia
7 Sri Lanka
8 Richmond
9 Van Diemen's Land
10 Oslo

70   General Knowledge

1 Lake Nyasa
2 Limpopo
3 Illinois
4 Cevennes
5 Helsinki
6 Niagara Falls
7 A lake in Florida
8 Olympus
9 Balalaika
10 Mount Cook

71   British Isles

1 Chesil Bank
2 Lough Neagh, Northern Ireland
3 Holyhead
4 Orkney Islands
5 Kinder Scout
6 Isle of Man
7 Skye
8 East Sussex
9 Armagh
10 Aran Islands

72   General Knowledge

1 Music City
2 Amnesty International
3 Lake Lugano
4 Spain
5 Arkhangelsk
6 Fort Knox
7 Limerick
8 The Cordilleras
9 Elsinore
10 Bataan

73   The Mediterranean

1   Balearics
2   Cyprus
3   Naxos
4   Corsica
5   Sicily
6   Aegean Sea
7   Paphos
8   Italy
9   Malta
10   Lipari Islands

74   General Knowledge

1   Argentina
2   Black Sea
3   Greece
4   St Louis
5   Italian
6   Alaska
7   Louis Bleriot
8   Tenerife
9   Chile
10   Hamburger

75   Where Is It?

1   Ukraine
2   Morocco
3   Belgium
4   Solomon Islands
5   Mexico
6   Romania
7   Brazil
8   The Sahara desert in Mali
9   Morocco
10   Ukraine

76   General Knowledge

1   China
2   Mississippi
3   St Moritz
4   Hungary
5   Chinese-born American
6   St Albans
7   District of Colombia
8   Iran and Iraq
9   Ian Smith
10   Dry sherry

77   Volcanoes Around the World

1   Vesuvius
2   Argentina
3   Krakatoa
4   Paricutin
5   Stromboli
6   Etna
7   Cotopaxi
8   Mount St Helens
9   Hawaii
10   Mount Erebus

78   General Knowledge

1   New Mexico
2   Darling River
3   Naxos
4   Brittany
5   Sanskrit
6   Haiti
7   Brazil
8   Milan
9   Eisteddfod
10   The Curragh

79 Coups and Revolutions

1 Uganda
2 Hungary
3 James II
4 Sudan
5 Tiananmen Square
6 *Bounty*
7 Chile
8 Romania
9 Argentina
10 Russia

80 General Knowledge

1 Orly
2 2.5 m/8 ft
3 2000
4 Portugal
5 Diego Garcia
6 Dutch East Indies
7 Bentiu
8 Three Mile Island
9 The American Constitution
10 Aberystwyth

81 The Pacific

1 Melanesia
2 North Island
3 Ocean Island
4 Ellice Islands
5 Johnston Atoll
6 Arafura Sea
7 Society Islands
8 Friendly Islands
9 Queensland
10 Sea of Okhotsk

82 General Knowledge

1 Casablanca
2 Rhode Island
3 Pakistan
4 Pampas
5 Charlemagne Prize
6 South Africa
7 Japan
8 Pennsylvania
9 Canada
10 Brisbane

83 Deserts Around the World

1 Painted Desert
2 Chile
3 Kalahari desert
4 Nubian desert
5 Kara-Kum
6 Gobi
7 Sahara
8 Negev Desert
9 Mojave Desert
10 Deserts of North Africa and Arabia

84 General Knowledge

1 Burma, now Myanmar
2 Bermuda
3 Hawaii
4 Easter Island
5 Third World
6 Lanzarote
7 Electoral college
8 Milan
9 William McKinley
10 Aldershot

85 Wars Around the World

1 Korea
2 Dunkerque
3 Nürnberg
4 Czechoslovakia
5 Austria
6 Spain
7 Honduras and El Salvador
8 Gibraltar
9 Kuwait
10 Arnhem

86   General Knowledge

1 Browns Ferry
2 Portuguese
3 Berlin Wall
4 Potomac
5 Ottoman Empire
6 Federal government
7 Mexico
8 Amazon
9 Monaco
10 Loch Ness monster

87   India

1 Jodhpur
2 Calcutta
3 Bombay
4 Madras
5 Coromandel Coast
6 Ellora caves
7 Kashmir
8 Cochin
9 A mountain
10 Allahabad

88   General Knowle

1 Lourdes
2 Motor racing
3 Frog jumping
4 Democracy
5 Potato
6 1770
7 Friends of the Earth
8 Rio Grande
9 Dodo
10 Seismology

89   Canals Around the World

1 Caledonian Canal
2 Suez Canal
3 Welland Canal
4 Gota Canal
5 Grand Canal (Yun Ho)
6 Rideau Canal
7 Albert Canal
8 Panama
9 Grand Canal
10 Kiel Canal

90   General Knowledge

1 Juan Fernandez
2 North Dakota
3 Honolulu
4 *Glasnost*
5 A marsupial
6 Congress
7 Quito
8 Alcatraz
9 Carbon dioxide
10 Arbroath

The Low Countries

Netherlands
2 Polder
3 The Grand Duchy of
Luxembourg
4 Benelux
5 French
6 China
7 Belgium
8 Ghent
9 Bruxelles
10 Rotterdam

92   General Knowledge

1 Boston
2 Naples
3 Iraq
4 Germany
5 Delos
6 Sri Lanka
7 Martha's Vineyard
8 Aldeburgh
9 Asia
10 Arthur's Seat

93   Biblical Places

1 Jericho
2 Damascus
3 Canaan
4 Sistine Chapel in the Vatican,
Rome
5 Bethlehem
6 Judea
7 Mount Sinai
8 Tarsus
9 Armageddon
10 Sea of Galilee

94   General Knowledge

1 Prince William Sound
2 UK, USA, Russia, China, and
France
3 Limpopo
4 Greater Antilles
5 Knotted carpets
6 Czech Republic and Slovak
Republic
7 India
8 Grampians
9 Bay of Fundy
10 Long Island

95   Getting Around

1 France
2 Canadian-Pacific railway
3 Ferdinand Porsche
4 Denmark
5 Sweden
6 Limousine – worn by the
inhabitants of the province of
Limousin
7 Greyhound Bus Company
8 It was assisted by wind
9 Venice
10 Liberia

96   General Knowledge

1 Limoges
2 Tanzania
3 Kabul
4 Canada
5 Cologne
6 Shetlands
7 Bangkok
8 Baghdad
9 Danube
10 Brazil

97   Natural Disasters

1 An earthquake almost destroyed the city
2 Agadir
3 Bangladesh
4 Texas
5 Hekla
6 Cameroon
7 Avalanche
8 Bubonic plague
9 California
10 Bhopal

98   General Knowledge

1 Bikini Atoll
2 Bihar
3 Perth
4 Sirocco
5 Great Bermuda
6 Singapore – *Singa pura*
7 Uruguay
8 Lake Garda
9 Maine
10 Cyprus

99   Dire Straits

1 Strait of Malacca
2 Strait of Magellan
3 Formosa Strait
4 Davis Strait
5 Menai Strait
6 Strait of Gibraltar
7 Sicily
8 Bering Strait – after Vitus Bering
9 Cook Strait
10 Bosporus

100   General Knowledge

1 East Anglia
2 Lake Baikal
3 Gold mining
4 A Scottish island
5 Portugal
6 Malta
7 Table Mountain
8 Swords
9 Suez Canal
10 Sicily

101   China

1 Chang Jiang or Yangtse-Kiang
2 The Great Leap Forward
3 Yuan
4 Great Wall
5 Kunlun Shan
6 Manchuria
7 Chungking or Chongqing
8 Shanghai
9 Amoy
10 Kowloon

102   General Knowledge

1 Trinity College
2 Duisburg
3 Ekaterinburg
4 Baltic States
5 Bay of Bengal
6 Angola
7 Prince Edward Island
8 The Minch
9 New Orleans
10 Bahamas

obago
Bartlett Trench
Christopher Columbus
4 Barbuda
5 Dominica
6 Leeward Islands
7 Martinique
8 Havana
9 Antigua
10 Caribbean Community and
Common Market (CARICOM)

104   General Knowledge

1 Ethiopia
2 Liffey
3 Baja California
4 Bayeux
5 Pacific
6 Gibraltar
7 Parnassos
8 Pasadena
9 Switzerland
10 Dachau

105   Russia and the USSR

1 Lenin
2 Sakhalin Island
3 15
4 Traditional tea urn
5 Dnepr/Dnieper
6 Lakes
7 Adygea
8 Kiev
9 Lake Baikal
10 Armenia

106   General Knowledge

1 Indonesia
2 Fiji
3 Suez Canal
4 Czech Republic
5 Dover and Calais
6 Dalmatia
7 1960s
8 Samurai
9 Dogger Bank
10 Donegal

107   Capes Around
the World

1 Cape Canaveral
2 Cape St Vincent
3 San Lucas Cape
4 Chelyuskin Cape
5 Spain
6 Cape Horn
7 Cape Cod
8 Cape Wrath
9 Cape of Good Hope
10 Cap Gris-Nez

108   General Knowledge

1 Anglesey
2 Tennessee
3 Piraeus
4 Falkland Islands
5 Faroes
6 Gothenburg
7 Berlin
8 Elba
9 Barbados
10 India

1 Egypt
2 USA
3 Southern Spain
4 Battle of Hastings
5 Crécy
6 Midway Islands
7 Rorke's Drift
8 Little Bighorn
9 Denmark
10 Marathon

110   General Knowledge

1 Vancouver Island
2 Aye-aye
3 Farne Islands
4 Fars
5 Belgrade
6 Tropic of Cancer
7 Adirondack Mountains
8 Guyana
9 Delft
10 Seattle

111   Political Geography

1 Sierra Leone
2 USA and Canada
3 Borneo
4 Denmark
5 Hong Kong
6 San Marino
7 French Guiana
8 UK
9 Italy
10 France

112   General Kn

1 Honshu – main islands of
2 Punjab
3 Chester
4 China
5 Thailand
6 River Seine
7 Oregon
8 Schilling
9 Kampala
10 Denmark

113   Currencies
Around the World

1 Malaysia
2 Rouble
3 Athens
4 Rupee
5 Centimo
6 Zambia and Malawi
7 Danish krone
8 Argentina
9 Dinar
10 Peso

114   General Knowledge

1 Scilly Isles
2 Cyprus
3 Mount Rushmore
4 Mount Fuji
5 China
6 Germany
7 Dodge City
8 East Indies
9 Witch trials
10 Sheffield

Bridges Around the World

1 ridge of Sighs
London Bridge
3 Gladsesville Bridge
4 Rhine
5 Sweden
6 Venice
7 Montréal
8 New York
9 Orkney Causeway, also known as Churchill Barriers
10 Golden Gate Bridge

116 General Knowledge

1 Nanshan Islands
2 India
3 Vietnam
4 Winter Olympics
5 Dublin
6 John O'Groats
7 South Africa
8 Great Lakes
9 Amsterdam
10 Doldrums

117 Ancient Civilizations

1 Tunisia
2 Macedonia
3 Turkey
4 Gaul
5 Inca
6 Iraq
7 Egyptian
8 Crete
9 Babylon
10 Halicarnassus

118 General Knowledge

1 Northumberland
2 Czechoslovakia
3 Uruguay
4 Andorra
5 Maldives
6 Luzon Island in the Philippines
7 Macassar
8 Isle of Wight
9 Luxembourg
10 Hebrideans

119 Spain

1 Costa del Sol
2 Paella
3 Mantilla
4 Ebro
5 Andalusia
6 Zaragoza
7 Costa Blanca
8 Cortes
9 Majorca
10 Canary Islands

120 General Knowledge

1 Monaco
2 Paraguay
3 Port-au-Prince
4 Eire – Republic of Ireland
5 Barbados
6 Iceland
7 Federated States of Micronesia
8 Mountain ranges
9 Deccan
10 Djibouti

121   Tunnels and Passes

1   Italy and Austria
2   Khyber Pass
3   St Gothard Tunnel
4   Channel Tunnel
5   Austria
6   Uspallata Pass
7   France
8   Cumberland Gap
9   Honshu and Hokkaido
10   Switzerland and Italy

122   General Knowledge

1   Red, white, blue
2   The Bosporus
3   Bordeaux
4   Ottawa
5   Okinawa
6   Jordan
7   Damodar
8   Bath
9   Chile
10   Iberian Peninsula

123   Tourist Attractions

1   France
2   Moscow
3   Terracotta Army
4   Somerset
5   Copenhagen
6   Montreux
7   Denmark
8   The Alamo
9   Rome
10   Annaheim

124   General Kno

1   The Alps
2   Istanbul
3   Santiago
4   Madras
5   Grampian Mountains
6   Challenger Deep
7   Berne, Switzerland
8   Dorset
9   Morocco
10   Cambridge, England

125   Waterfalls Around the World

1   New Zealand
2   Zambezi
3   Switzerland
4   Yosemite
5   France
6   Victoria Falls
7   Five
8   Niagara Falls
9   Goat Island
10   Venezuela

126   General Knowledge

1   Avignon
2   Azores
3   Finland
4   Minsk
5   Vietnam
6   Milton Keynes
7   Philippines
8   Cymru
9   Chicago
10   New Hebrides

yern

Ibe

No Smoking

4 Helmut Kohl

5 Lower Saxony

6 1961

7 Ruhr Valley

8 Zugspitze

9 Bavaria

10 Black Forest

128   General Knowledge

1 Loire

2 Genoa

3 Tatra Mountains

4 Mogadishu

5 Norkapp

6 Lake Ohrid

7 Greenwich

8 Tokyo

9 Liechtenstein

10 Botswana

129   Central America

1 Honduras

2 Christopher Columbus

3 Nicaragua

4 Belize

5 Guatemala

6 Nicaragua

7 El Salvador

8 Costa Rica

9 Usumacinta River

10 Mosquito Coast

130   General Knowledge

1 France

2 Waveney

3 Danube

4 English

5 Rance

6 Riyadh

7 York

8 Nickel

9 South America – capital of Suriname

10 Scapa Flow

131   South Africa

1 Johannesburg

2 Lesotho

3 English

4 Drakensberg Mountains

5 Limpopo

6 Kimberley

7 1990

8 Bloemfontein

9 Sun City

10 Gold

132   General Knowledge

1 Georgetown

2 Bourgogne

3 Sinai Peninsula

4 Rhine

5 Leningrad

6 Red Sea

7 Portuguese

8 Le Touquet

9 Port Louis

10 Mongolia

133   Name the Country

1 Norway
2 Chad
3 Costa Rica
4 Vietnam
5 Peru
6 Monaco
7 Seychelles
8 Austria
9 Myanmar
10 New Zealand

134   General Knowledge

1 Egypt
2 Gambia
3 New Guinea
4 Rabat
5 Lagan
6 Australia
7 Norway
8 Peruvian
9 Gaza Strip
10 Java

135   World Leaders

1 Fidel Castro
2 Haiti
3 Portugal
4 David Ben-Gurion
5 Luxembourg
6 Ceylon, now Sri Lanka
7 Arkansas
8 Egypt
9 Robben Island
10 Australia

136   General Kn⌐

1 The Dardanelles
2 Rome
3 Adriatic Sea
4 Madrid
5 Greenland
6 Ossetia
7 Old World
8 Knossos
9 Kazakhstan
10 Hawaii

137 Arts Around the World

1 Siena
2 St Petersburg
3 Milan
4 The Louvre in Paris
5 Spanish
6 Venice
7 El Greco
8 Pablo Picasso
9 Florence
10 Milos – Venus de Milo

138   General Knowledge

1 Namib Desert
2 Olduvai Gorge
3 Tunis
4 Comoros
5 Dutch Guiana
6 Murmansk
7 Spain
8 French
9 Kathmandu
10 Cambodia

Traditions Around the World

amplona
Money
3 Rio de Janeiro
4 Nottingham
5 Ice skates
6 Oberammergau
7 Beer
8 The Haka
9 Lerwick in the Shetland Islands
10 New Orleans

140   General Knowledge

1 Korea
2 Spain
3 Ngorongoro Crater
4 Bight of Biafra
5 Balkan Peninsula
6 Wales
7 Tripoli
8 Islamabad
9 Windermere
10 Honshu

141   Wildernesses Around the World

1 Vinson Massif
2 Katmai National Park
3 Rub'al Khali
4 Outback
5 Tundra
6 Barren Grounds
7 Lapland
8 Siberia
9 White Sea
10 Death Valley

142   General Knowledge

1 Netherlands
2 South Africa
3 Malawi
4 Guernsey
5 Horn of Africa
6 Australian
7 Sweden
8 Tehran
9 Denmark Strait
10 Tay

143   World Demography

1 California
2 China
3 Libya
4 Singapore
5 Last – 50th
6 Monaco
7 Birmingham
8 Vatican City
9 Bombay
10 Netherlands

144   General Knowledge

1 Missouri
2 Lake Rudolf
3 Five
4 Alabama
5 Guadalajara
6 Agulhas
7 Northern Ireland
8 Hawaii
9 Namibia
10 Brooklyn

145   Dress Around the World

1 Sarong
2 Poncho
3 Duffel coat
4 Sporran
5 India
6 Fez
7 Lederhosen
8 Feet
9 Yashmak
10 Astrakhan

146   General Knowledge

1 Moskva
2 Lake Albert
3 Malay Peninsula
4 South African
5 Neva
6 Porcelain
7 Anglesey
8 Philadelphia
9 Libya
10 St Helena

147   Dams Around the World

1 Kariba Dam
2 26 km/16 mi
3 Grand Coulee Dam
4 India
5 Ijsselmeer
6 Egypt
7 Switzerland
8 Hoover Dam
9 Zambezi
10 Aswan High Dam

148   General Knowledge

1 Nagasaki
2 La Mancha
3 Lausanne
4 Lincoln
5 Portugal
6 Calabria
7 Africa
8 Spanish
9 Australia
10 Botswana

149 Hills Around the World

1 Black Hills
2 Somerset
3 Cotswolds
4 Rome
5 Volga
6 Bunker Hill
7 Chilterns
8 Myanmar
9 Mount of Olives
10 Monte Cassino

150   General Knowledge

1 Fair Isle
2 New Jersey
3 Cairo
4 Zambia
5 Spanish
6 Muscat
7 The Trossachs
8 Kansas
9 Pentland Firth
10 Netherlands